A WONDER IN THE GARDEN

A Wonder in the Garden

The World of Nature Just Outside Our Doors

DR TONY KENDLE

UNITED WRITERS
Cornwall

UNITED WRITERS PUBLICATIONS LTD
Ailsa, Castle Gate, Penzance, Cornwall.
www.unitedwriters.co.uk

British Library Cataloguing in Publication Data:
A catalogue record for this book is
available from the British Library.

ISBN 9781852002022

Printed and bound in Great Britain by
United Writers Publications Ltd.,
Cornwall.

For Jane

Photographic and artistic credits:

Rick Squirrel: '*After frondescence the leaf eaters get fresh salad at last*'; '*Anthocyanin gives the red leaf colour*'; '*Clouds and trees are fractal shapes*'; '*Come eat me; spread my seeds*'; '*Compositae are lots of small flowers jammed together*'; '*Dusts make sunsets more colourful*'; '*Flowers give gifts to pollinators*'; '*Flowers must provide safe and stable landing spots*'; '*Leaves breathe through pores*'.

Diana Heyne: '*Anthocyanins become more visible as chlorophyll fades*'; '*Butterflies need our help*'; '*Butterfly on lichen*'; '*Clock and compass from gathered leaves*'; '*Dew spangled web*'; '*Fallen leaves do much good*'; '*Fungi and epiphytes*'; '*Ginkgo leaf and hoverfly*'; '*Ginkgo leaves*'.

Jan Watterson: '*Hart's-tongue fern*'; '*Ivy flower*'; '*Tree returning to air*'.

Malcolm Sheppard: '*Fungi are not plants or animals*'.

Jane Stoneham: '*Frondescence*'; '*Ants patrol and guard their home trees*'; '*Ants patrol and protect*'; '*Bonfire Moss*'; '*Ferns have spores not seeds*'; '*Flowers guide the pollinators to their nectar*'; '*Lichens on a garden bench*'; '*Seeds preparing for flight*'.

Susan Warner: *Three photographs of her mandalas.*

Sharon Willoughby: '*Puddles are mirrors and portals*'.

Adam Burton: '*Mosses are also fractal shapes*'; '*Wistman's Wood, the temperate rainforest*'; '*Trees summon the rain they depend on*'.

Susan Humphries: '*School in a wood*'.

Rebecca Stoneham: '*Ivy in winter*'.

Eden Project: '*Bodelva pit before Eden Project*'; '*Eden Project today*'; '*Eden gardens today*'.

Contents

Foreword

by Tim Smit
Founder of the Eden Project
& the Lost Gardens of Heligan

I first met Tony Kendle in 1996 in the home of a great mutual friend, Peter Thoday, who had been a teacher to Tony at Bath University and a mentor to me in the restoration of The Lost Gardens of Heligan, in Cornwall. Peter's deep experience of the horticulture of the Victorian era saw him co-present 'The Victorian Kitchen Garden' (BBC) and he helped us to restore Heligan, to perform the full opera of horticulture.

Elsewhere in the UK, while we were restoring Heligan, Tony was cutting his teeth with Professor Tony Bradshaw, establishing how to transform barren, degraded land, such as spoil heaps, landfill sites and brown field industrial sites, to life. He would be building a palette of techniques for soil creation, companion planting, and plant remediation using what is called phytoremediation, (where plants absorb harmful minerals into themselves) so with every harvest of them the land becomes less poisoned.

At Heligan we started to learn some really important lessons. Initially our success was accompanied by a public fanfare and all the popular lifestyle magazines from then on in were full of articles about growing your own and, isn't it wonderful and healthy to live this bucolic life? In short, a middle class urbanised country idyll! What we were learning was something very different; that historically, before refrigeration, April was the dying month. It was then that you ran out of food before the seasons had brought forth new abundance. It was here in this story that you started to truly understand the scientific excellence of the Head Gardeners and their teams. They had to master the art of planting on south facing walls for early crops, and on the northern, more shaded walls for late crops. They needed to know how to both force and retard the seasons, not only by using specific planting times but also through covering in the dark and so on. At Heligan they grew a huge range of vegetables and fruits because each variety ripened at a slightly different time, and some of the fruit was grown not because of its excellence of flavour but because, normally stored in a straw filled wooden tray, it could 'keep' for a very long time without rotting. These people, for all the fact that the modern world, in its ignorance, does not acknowledge the truth of it, were applied scientists every bit as important as those in the medical, pharmacy or engineering professions, and possibly more important!

I dwell on the two backgrounds of Tony, a horticulturist and soil scientist/ecologist, and our observations at Heligan, because in these two experiences you can start to clearly make out the evolving skill sets that would be needed to draw together a horticultural team capable of remediating a degraded landscape, and then bringing it back to spectacular life with the greatest exhibition of economic plants (plants known to be overtly useful to humankind) ever. Now the magic combination had met and the Eden Project was born, with Peter Thoday and Philip MacMillan Browse as Horticultural Directors previously from Heligan, and overseeing the whole procedure was Tony Kendle.

We had become friends after the meeting in 1996 and had met many times since as we teased out the narrative of the Eden Project, and Tony had to convince constructors and banks that you could actually deliver on something that had never been done before.

Tony oversaw the creation of the greatest soil manufacturing project in history, making upwards of 85,000 tonnes of the stuff in a nearby pit using giant diggers as his equivalent of a Moulinex mixer, where the dance of the diggers brought life into being, and slowly but surely, the sterile clay pit would receive the appropriate mixture of clay waste, mushroom and domestic composts, chicken manure and so on. Once placed it would be pinioned under coir matting or hemp sacking to prevent erosion from the rain. Then millions of plants were brought in and planted through the material, so that once it had rotted the roots would keep the hillsides and banks from slipping.

Back at the nursery, Tony's team were experimenting like maniacs to ensure the right mixes were provided for each plant. A remarkable fact is that of the initial plantings of c6000 species and several million in number, into a previously untested medium, less than 1% would perish, which is an extraordinary testament to the team.

Obviously, in remaking land you are not recreating ecosystems, you are enabling new ones to create themselves. We understood the need for water and how it should be managed. We understood, too, that it would take a number of years for the plants to develop a proper cycle of leaf fall to decay back to self-nourishment, such that for the first five years there would need to be a feeding regime that supplemented the organic litter on the ground.

What was the biggest surprise? Tony had put in place a regimen of natural pesticides and biological controls. Nematodes imported to eat the bugs and scales and so on. We had spent c£250,000 getting our two biomes (the humid tropics and the Mediterranean) into biological balance when disaster struck – we discovered the larvae of the banana moth. This is a dreaded pest, because the caterpillars live in the roots and eat them before appearing on the soil to fly off as moths, leaving the banana plant dying. Against our wishes, we were forced by DEFRA to use a chemical spray in an area after previously only using biological controls. It would be a deep lesson in biology and ecology. An area 1x1 sq metres was sprayed, killing every living thing. . . We waited. . . Every child is taught the phrase 'Nature abhors a vacuum'. . . and so it proved in spades. Ants bred at an improbable speed, moved in, bred then bred some more, and in less than six weeks the Humid Tropics were under siege from them. It took us nearly three years to get the ants under control.

I mention this example of nature's reply to mankind's interference, because it is exactly this sort of juxtaposition we become aware of as we enter Tony's Garden. Tony is describing an arena that could be as big as a planet or as small as a postage stamp. However, the principles remain the same, and it is important before you enter Tony's magic kingdom, that you realise the nature of the world you are entering and the fact that you are exploring a restless, constantly adapting world in which we all have a part. Once you stop desiring the starring role and embrace the humility needed to truly listen and learn, you may come to a spiritual awakening: that you are as much a part of this life as what you are looking at. I won't spoil the narrative thrust of the book, but if you dare to concentrate and not switch off at lichens, mosses, slimes and scales, you will find that they and the Mycorrhiza that make up the fungal underworld are no less than wormholes into other worlds.

12

Furthermore, the lessons learnt here make you think about what the applications for such new awakenings could have in the way we live in the future. Bear in mind we have been around for merely a sneeze compared to these super adaptable ancestors of ours.

I began by describing the journeys that got Tony and myself to Eden. You will have understood by now what a vital leader he was there. Just as important, is to understand the narrative that moves from small to big then back to small again. Above I have described the horticulturist's art and the ecologist's understanding. I have done this as I want you to thoroughly enjoy this marvellous book, because I am not sure anyone has ever written a book quite like this, or as good as this, before. It is almost like a Rough Guide to your garden, but strangely describing it as a whole each time before focussing on the specific. In the hands of Tony you will understand the magnificent strength and fragility of the soil and the natural environment. You will have introductions to its cast of players and be left, I hope, with some profound thoughts on the role of human stewardship, and a dawning realisation that we have so much to learn, for if we damage the environment we are damaging ourselves, and our fundamental well-being; our reset button lies in being amongst it, being a part, not apart, from the Natural World. Enjoy this delicious and important book and keep it on your bedside table as you would a spiritual work, for it is refreshing in every sense of the word.

TBS Jan. 2021

Introduction

The Cultivation of Nature's Splendour

"The world is full of magic things patiently waiting for our senses to grow sharper." William Butler Yeats.

"Mysterious and little known organisms live within walking distance of where you sit. Splendour awaits in minute proportions." E.O. Wilson – Biophilia

The starting question – What are gardens for?

There are many things we often take for granted, not least the fact that we have gardens at all. Have you ever stood at the window, looked onto your patch and wondered – "why is this small part of the vast and complex living Earth in my care?" What is it there for, what gifts does it bring me and what gifts can I bring to it?

As a member of the team that created the Eden Project in Cornwall I was tasked with a technical challenge that proved to be a philosophical challenge as well. With my background as a researcher of restoring mine sites, Tim Smit challenged me: "Can we make a garden of wonders in this sterile pit?" We stood and peered over a crumbling edge of the moonscape, a worked-out china clay quarry, but with lorries still rumbling across a stark

14

white mud, and I mumbled, 'Yes, we can.' In hindsight my confidence came not just from my research but also from seeing at first hand the astonishing resilience and robustness with which nature has proven able to reclaim, regrow and regenerate places devastated by our worst destructive efforts: from Chernobyl to the psychedelically coloured mines of Parys Mountain in Anglesey and Rio Tinto in Spain, I have seen repeatedly that nature has creative responses to our worst excesses.

So, after a few sleepless nights, I relaxed and reiterated with increasing confidence – yes, a garden will grow there. But would it be a wondrous garden, or just a few patches of green clinging to life against all odds in a barren wasteland? That question ignited further debate – what makes a garden, anyway?

What makes a garden?

Few people, whether gardeners, naturalists or managers of the countryside are faced with fully erased landscapes. Whatever land we become engaged with, nearly always we inherit a community of life, a vibrant ecology of relationships already there. These ecologies of place reflect a rich history of colonisation, growth and mutual support. We are rarely required to ask some key questions. 'What could this place be? What should it be? What is best for this landscape, the Earth and those that visit or join the community in the future?

With Eden's scalped and pared-back environment, poor in wonders, but overflowing with unrealised potential, there were no existing communities of life or landscapes to grow with. So we had to ask – if it will be a garden of sorts, what could it be, what should it be? What are gardens there for, anyway?

Most answers promoted by contemporary culture are utilitarian rather than inspirational. Our gardens, we are told, are 'outdoor rooms', an extension of our normal lives – a place for entertaining sometimes, often a dining space or maybe a play space for the kids. Gardens are also for display, they are an important part of the 'front', the facades of our homes and lives that we use to represent us to the world.

Gardens show who we are

Don't underestimate how much gardens advertise who you are and what you care for. The best illustration of this were the grand estates of the 16th to 18th centuries. For the rich and powerful, the extent and quality of the garden was the outward show of the owner's wealth, education and influence – to be someone, your kitchen gardens had to grow the latest varieties, the ornamental borders needed to display the latest plant hunter discoveries.

The landscape needed to bear the signature of the most fashionable designers and be peppered with statues that demonstrated the highest classical education and wit. But beware – if you were too showy, too ready to display your power, wealth and culture, you could bring down the displeasure of the crown, who might see this display as a power play and even a threat. Heads could be lost if gardens were too showy. Still, today, we feel pressure to keep our plots in 'appropriate' condition for passing eyes. We no longer need to display a classical education, but we do need to show that we can manage our property to a basic standard.

I would like to argue an alternative view – the garden is not there to be 'useful' or display our status or sense of responsibility; the front is less important than the substance. If we are lucky enough to have one that we can access, a garden can be there to be a reserve and an observatory, a place where we can learn about life and somewhere we can give something back.

Start with what you've got

Unlike our experience at the Eden Project, you are not likely to be faced with a fully erased landscape. However, if you live in a new build home you may well have a plot that has little growing in it, offering only potential, and frequently a soil that has been through upheavals during the construction, with much of its life squashed into mud.

On top of that the COVID lockdown has erased some things too. The normal trips to nearby green spaces have become less straightforward and, for many of us, less frequent pleasures. Our horizons have had to change – places just a small distance away became inaccessible; travel to landscapes of grand splendour and exotic wildlife became faint memories. We have had to refocus, look harder at the nearby things, observe more. Our connections to nature have been weakened and we are the poorer for it.

After long fireside debates, we agreed the role and purpose for our new Eden garden germinating amidst the destruction. This was not to be a place for show, it would be a place of wonders, somewhere to encounter life's diversity, richness and resilience, somewhere to celebrate, be grateful for what the world of nature gives us and. . . hopefully somewhere to reflect on what we could give back. To that end we also agreed that it shouldn't be too perfect, too manicured, it should always be a 'project' rather than an established estate.

A story of resilience and recovery

Although I had trained in a parks department and was familiar with precision displays of flowering excess, our challenge here was different and needed to be carefully judged. I wanted the visitor to say in awe, "How on earth is that growing here?" rather than, "Those flowers are beautiful." The very contrast of the moonscape of mining and the beauty of nature could give our visitors a different experience – the beauty and grace of resilience and recovery rather than of manicured perfection.

Given the rising tide of concern about climate chaos and a coming mass extinction that were already manifesting as a suite of new anxieties, we felt that a garden that inspired hope and awe was a genuine contribution to the world in a way that another collection of shrubs and bedding could not be. It was also a purpose that honoured and made full use of the site's history and wounds, rather than wandering into the role and territory of the RHS and National Trust.

I would like to offer these ideas and Eden experiences as options for your germinating gardens too.

The purpose of this book

In common understanding, today the word 'forest' refers to extensive tracts of woodland, but we learn from scholars such as Oliver Rackham that originally the word had a different meaning. A forest was a legal definition of land that was outside of the norm, in the sense that it was subject to different laws, usually designated to give extra privileges to the rich and powerful. Most of these estates were preserved as hunting lands and exploitation by others was strictly controlled, this meant that they incidentally became sanctuaries for wildlife and richly wooded – hence our current perception of what a forest is.

I propose we declare the same for the common estates, our gardens – let them also be outside the norm, sanctuaries too, and preserved for hunting – joy and wonder rather than deer – for all of us, not the privileged few.

The more that we connect with nature and begin to understand how the lives of other earthlings unfold, especially those that live just outside our windows, the greater the chance of positive feedback – we learn how to help our natural neighbours and in doing so we help ourselves.

Part of this understanding is technical – we need the insights that science can give us. But alongside science, just as important, are the core skills of all natural philosophers. Observation and curiosity are skills that are not innate or fixed, they can be cultivated and enhanced.

With these stories of the world near to us, I hope to see more gardeners make a shift, go back to basics and do what they are not supposed to – worry less about perfect flowers and tidy lawns but rather welcome and come to enjoy the messy, dirty nature of nature, let wonders grow around us, and grow as people too. Specifically, I believe that our gardens should:

Cultivate wonder rather than decoration.
Not be influenced too much by what neighbours or
    onlookers think.
Not follow the latest fashions or 'lifestyle' promotions.
    – we should treat with caution what most magazines and
    TV programmes tell us to do, they rarely champion the
    messy nature of nature.
In particular we should not be totally dependent on
    big companies, or even big charities for food, beauty,
    health and conservation of abundance. Life is ours to
    live and also ours to care for.

Instead, I hope you want to learn enough of the gardening basics, including observation, to be able to make your own choices, to declare your personal place, however small, as your unique opportunity to express a love of life rather than a love of 'lifestyle' or consumption. It could be your garden or the small square of pavement and the street tree outside that you adopt and cherish.

When I was small it was the mosses and velvet mites of our front garden walls that was my wilderness – peering into the emerald caves I imagined shrinking for adventures like the TV show 'Land of the Giants' – this was when I first realised that our garden ecosystems were as full of splendour as any rainforest shown on TV. At a micro-scale mosses can be as complex as forests – peer inside, ideally with a hand lens or magnifying glass, and you will find that there is a world within. Tiny things living in a fairytale landscape, green castles and caves are their homes.

I hope that armed with passion, more understanding and a little inspiration you too will want to have adventures in the nearby wonders and cultivate splendours. The purpose of this book is to learn in detail of the rich biodiversity that lives just beyond our doorsteps, a source of wonders that can do much to boost our health and understanding of our environments.

I have framed much of this around gardens, but everything here applies equally to nearby green patches, whether parks or wastelands, the edgelands of derelict plots, industrial estates or just street trees and the tiny ecosystems of the cracks in pavements.

You might notice that in this book I have chosen to capitalise the common names of trees, flowers and small creatures. The common naming convention is that capitals are reserved for 'proper' nouns, the things we declare as most significant. I believe that if a street name deserves a capital letter, then trees and creatures do too.

Chapter 1

Our Primary Partners in Gardening – the Plants

Understandably most people would say that gardens are all about plants. Whilst it is true that plants are the foundation, they are just the start of the story. Plants underpin a diverse and complex, mutually supporting mosaic of life that constitutes countless other members of our garden ecosystem – fungi, birds, microbes, insects and other animals. The garden is where we meet and can even care for many of them.

Strictly speaking you don't have to know how plants work to appreciate them, but understanding more about them will open a door to more enjoyment and improve your chances of helping if things go wrong.

The cure for plant blindness

Maybe it is because our culture never openly honours plants, or because our schooling can mistake the naming of parts for understanding, but most of us grow up with little real awareness of how plants work and why we need them. This is probably less true of keen gardeners and nature lovers, but in some people this lack of awareness is so extreme that they can become effectively 'blind' to plants.

In 1998, two scientists in South Carolina, USA coined the term 'plant blindness' to mean 'the inability to see or notice the plants in one's own environment, leading to the inability to recognise the importance of plants in the biosphere and in human affairs.'

Plant blindness also comprises an 'inability to appreciate the aesthetic and unique biological features' of plants and 'the misguided, anthropocentric ranking of plants as inferior to animals, leading to the erroneous conclusion that they are unworthy of human consideration.'

Before we explore how to address this, we should ask "does it matter?"

I think it does for these reasons: Firstly, if we remain blind to the amazing ways that plants work, we miss out on lots of joy, wonder and inspiration. Also, if we remain blind to the foundation of our daily existence – the things that give us food, clean water, air to breathe and many of the things we depend on, we may fail to protect them and thus make our own lives and future more precarious. Our survival and flourishing become things we can no longer cultivate for ourselves, instead they have to be sold to us. Plant blindness disempowers us – it makes it harder to be active agents in our lives. We remain dependent on others for everything we need – food, water, beauty, health and, one day, maybe, clean air.

So, why not drop the blindfolds, come to see and understand the plants for your own sake as well as theirs.

Plants and people, much more in common than we realise

Since we are unlikely to love what seems alien to us, maybe the first step is understanding our commonalities. Plants are more like us than you may have ever imagined; in fact, we all share common ancestry. In the distant past every single person and every single plant all have a common ancestor. We are all related to each other. We are family.

Look around your house – every person, every cat, dog, hamster, and every house plant all share a common relative in prehistory. All life on earth diverges from one source. Isn't that a wonder to brighten your day?

It may seem hard to believe at first but the more we learn about plants, the clearer it becomes how much they have in common with us. I studied plant science and horticulture in the 1980s when this dimension of plant lives was not much considered. At that time agriscience was becoming obsessed with molecules and genetic modification. This emerging technology framed plants as little more than living machines – push the right buttons, insert the right genes and they can be made to do whatever you want them to.

Since then, scientists have discovered, and continue to discover, amazing new insights into how plants function – insights that undermine the machine model and reinstate plants as living beings with their unique ways of life and complex relationships too. Understanding more of these relationships will be the basis of the next great biological revolution – we learn increasingly that there are no such things as isolated individuals.

Every living being, including you, is a community, an amalgam of diverse organisms working together like an orchestra, known as a 'superorganism'. Darwin didn't know this and we will need to recraft our model of evolution. The 'fittest' that get selected are not the tough and most aggressive competitors, the fittest are the best communicators and collaborators. The gene manipulators will also need to rethink their models – changing the genes of one player in a team will prove insufficient, it will be enhancing the communities that matters. When we learn how to do this we will revolutionise health, and farming too.

Surely this in itself is another source of wonder and hope – after centuries of research, great revelations are still unfolding. Every young scientist-to-be still has uncharted seas to explore; undiscovered wonders still lie under every leaf and stone.

Plants – what are they up to?

To help appreciate plants fully it is useful to know at least a little of how they work and what they do all day, every day. Probably the single most important thing that plants do is that they feed themselves and everything else in the world by photosynthesis.

Photosynthesis – weaving a world from air

Using the simple chemicals of water and carbon dioxide and powered by energy from sunlight, plants can assemble more complex compounds – sugars, starches, and proteins. These compounds are used to build their own bodies and the fruits, vegetables, fibres and timbers we rely on to build our own bodies and our civilisations.

We understand it intellectually, maybe, but have you ever really reflected on the wonder that surrounds us everywhere? Out of odourless, invisible gases and sunlight, every day the plants weave a solid world of living things rich with a vibrancy of aroma, colour and movement. (Incidentally, this too is something they learnt from their supporting community – it was bacteria who invented photosynthesis first.)

All flesh is grass

Almost every living thing builds its body thanks to photosynthesis. As the bible says – 'all flesh is grass'. All flesh is grass, plants are the base of the food chain, everything else is just repackaging.

Grass is made from earth, wind, rain and light – so we are all made of earth, wind, rain and light woven together into substance.

David Haskall writes 'Atmosphere and plant make each other: plant as a temporary crystallisation of carbon; air as a product of 400 million years of forest breath. Neither tree nor air is independent.'

As part of the process of photosynthesis, the plants breathe in carbon dioxide – removing it from the air where it is a dangerous greenhouse gas. They keep the carbon and breathe back out oxygen that we all depend on. The carbon detached from the oxygen is reassembled and used to make the food, colour, sound and solid structures that the plants, and we, need.

Not all of the carbon that plants take in is kept by them – some is given to the soil. Plants feed the soil in two main ways:

One is by 'root exudates'. This may sound gross but this is food donated by the roots for the creatures that keep the soil and plants healthy and in turn these creatures feed birds and larger animals too. This soil carbon also becomes the 'glue' that binds soil particles into crumbs, creating the well-drained structure that roots need. This carbon that joins the soil is essential for a healthy world.

Secondly, every so often, plants contribute larger amounts of organic matter to soil when they die – sometimes they die wholly, like if a tree is taken by a storm or disease or fire. Unlike us, plants have a modular body – they can lose bits without being life threatening, which is how they survive browsing animals and pruning too, so usually plants die gradually and in pieces. Bits of fine root die every day, leaves and petals fall to the soil surface.

b

Plants, the great collaborators

Because they cannot move to get things done, plants also have to be masters of partnership. They collaborate with many other organisms to meet their needs. And because they can't move quickly enough to look for the partners themselves, plants have learnt a different skill, they know how to summon their partners to them. Usually this collaboration gives rewards to the partner and in this way the plants support an ecosystem of mutual health.

Some of the key collaborations are ones we all depend on:

Flowers summon pollinators to help them reproduce; without them, no seed, no crops, no food, no future.

Fruits summon animals to help them move their seed to new places; without them no migrations, no adjustment to changing climate, no escaping disaster.

Not all collaborations are benign in the garden. For example, tree-eating fungi collaborate with fungi-eating beetles that have evolved special baskets, called mycangia, for carrying the fungal spores to a new host – that means more fungi and more food for the beetles, but sadly fewer trees too.

In a counter move, wounded plants can also summon defensive allies which will include ones that control the beetle. It all goes round in a big circle. Life finds a way.

Possibly their most amazing trick, by releasing compounds that help fine mists coalesce and turn into larger drops, trees can summon the rain we all depend on. Rain makes trees possible, trees help create the rain in turn.

The sensory world of plants

As I was explaining the partnership skills of plants to a visitor at Eden Project, she asked a crucial question: "Do plants feel things, do they know what is happening to them?" It is a deeply important and perceptive question. Of course you can't sustain complex partnerships if you have no idea of what's afoot in your community – plants need and do have sophisticated senses.

We rarely think of plants as being aware of the world around them. Yet discovering what they sense and understand is one of the most exciting new fields in plant science. Perhaps not surprising since we share a common evolutionary ancestor, plants have several senses that we can directly relate to.

Plants are not just inanimate objects in the landscape, they do know what is happening and can change their behaviour accordingly. It is well proven that they have senses like vision, smell, touch, and taste and these senses are essential to their survival, as they are to us. Let's take a look at the sensory world of plants.

Can plants see?

Plants have sight. For a moment, ignore the structures – eyelids, lenses, etc. At the most fundamental level, our light sensing ability relies on proteins and pigments in specialised cells that fire a neural signal when light hits them. Plants have no light sensing structures like eyes, but they do have pigments, in fact they have more kinds of light reactive pigments than people do. Whilst plants don't use their 'sight' to interpret fine detail, there are still similarities in how we all use our ability to see light.

Plant 'vision' tends to get overlooked because, as we have seen already, for plants light is also the fuel for making food. The fact that they use light to photosynthesise is so fundamentally important to life on Earth, it is often all that we get taught about a plant's light perception. Yet plants use light in several other ways too. A plant may respond to change by gradually altering its growth rate or its direction of growth. The slow movements that plants make towards or away from a stimulus, such as light, are known as tropisms. Tropisms are controlled with the help of hormones called growth regulators, that cause the growth to speed up or slow down or trigger different structures to form.

Plants can also sense the direction that light is coming from. At a very slow pace they use this as a means of directing their growth – most plants grow towards light sources to get more food. They do this either by leaning or sending shoots and runners to the brightest patch. This movement towards light is called phototropism.

Another kind of phototropism is shown in how sunflowers twist to follow the sun – this maximises the visibility of the flowers to passing pollinators. Watching flowers turn is a quick and easy way to demonstrate that plants can 'see'.

Plants can also sense the duration of light and dark during the day – to do this they must have, and do have, some form of simple memory and means of measuring the passage of time. This response to light duration is known as photoperiodism.

Plants can also determine changes in the light spectrum, in particular varying amounts of infrared and ultraviolet. Plants use day-length and light spectrum changes to gather information about the passing of the seasons. This triggers many behavioural changes – telling them when to flower, when to develop fruits and seeds, when to drop leaves, and telling the seeds when it is safe to germinate because winter has gone.

Seeds can also tell if they are buried in soil or are in deep shade – they wait until the soil is turned or the canopy opens so they see light before they germinate. A classic example of this is red Poppy seed, millions of which were resting in the soil and became exposed to light when the Flanders fields of northern France were bombed, bathing the fields in red blooms later that summer.

The next obvious question is where are the plant's eyes? In early experiments, Charles Darwin used 'blindfolds' (really he did) to establish that the part of the plant that 'sees where the sun is' is not the leaves but the growing tip of the shoot.

Do plants know how warm it is?

Linked to their ability to perceive seasonal change by light, plants also use temperature to help measure the progress of the seasons. Vernalisation is the word given to the cold experience that plants need each year to know that winter has come and passed. Vernalisation helps break dormancy and trigger flower bud formation. If they do not get the right winter experience, they can get confused about the season, growth is poor and flowering is reduced. Amongst the worries brought by climate change is that some plants, such as apples, will not get cold enough to flower and fruit as they should.

Another temperature response is called stratification. Cold in winter followed by increasing warmth is how seeds know spring has come. This acts as a stimulus for germination, as it tells the seed when it is safe to come out of hibernation.

Do plants sleep?

Not only do plants sense the passing of the seasons, they sense the passing of day and night. Like us they have a circadian rhythm, and at night, like us, the plants do go to sleep. This is probably a shared behaviour that traces back to our earliest common ancestors who evolved in a world of changing light and dark.

Plants sleep perhaps because they are tired. Because plants don't look active at speeds we register, we rarely appreciate that they are working all day. The work they do is making food and products for every other being to use, and also pumping – all day long they pump water from the earth back to the clouds. They are the link from earth to sky. All day long they also pump carbon from the air into the ground, where it is safer for it to be, and in the process they release oxygen for us to breathe.

As the sun sets, no more food is to be made and less water loss means less water pumping through the stem – this is time to rest.

The study of the plants' nighttime behaviour is still evolving. Only the latest technology has allowed us to see that trees actually hang their tired branches lower at night.

In people it has been found that our daily rhythm influences lots of aspects of our lives, our quality of life, our immune system, our susceptibility to certain illnesses – even cancer and obesity, sex drive and fatigue. We are only beginning to understand these systems in plants – maybe their own immune systems fluctuate through the day – something else for scientists-to-be to discover.

Some plants use the signal of approaching night to fold away flowers or other parts they don't need in darkness – essentially, they tuck themselves up for bed. This tucking up at night is called nyctinasty.

Not every plant follows the same strategy. Whilst most pollinators are active in the day, some prefer the night shift – moths, beetles and night-flying bees included. Rather than compete for attention in the daytime when most other flowers are shouting for attention, some plants specialise in attracting night flyers. These night flowering plants tend to share certain characteristics: The flower colour may be of a hue that stands out in low light – think of the luminous yellow of Evening

Primrose. Others may have not bothered investing in show at all, instead producing small, inconspicuous flowers and relying more heavily on scent to attract their pollinators – Night-scented Stock is one of this group.

Why do plants smell?

Many night flowering plants are amongst the most richly scented of the plant world – they rely on the scent travelling far enough to attract pollinators that can't see them. For the plant the fragrance of a flower is not decorative, it is a message, an important communication that must get through.

One of the most important emerging fields in biology is how nature is communicating and coordinating essential collaborations. Without doubt the key system for communication is using scent. Every known group of living things use scent as a language to communicate. It seems that scent communication is more widespread than sound and vision as a way of sending messages.

As far as we know there are only certain creatures that communicate by sound – mammals, birds, insects, fish and even bacteria have been found to do so, but every class of creature communicates by smell – even plants and fungi too – yes, even mushrooms have a sense of smell!

David Haskell writes:

'Aroma is the primary language of trees. They talk with molecules, conspiring with one another, beckoning fungi, scolding insects, and whispering to microbes. Aroma is also our primal tongue, a direct link to memory and emotion, an inheritance from the communicative networks that sustained the first cells. The receptors in our nasal passages are ready to listen. We have over one hundred different olfactory receptors, able to discern at least ten thousand odours. The English language is too meagre to categorize this multiplicity, but our bodies know how to respond.'

31

As well as plants and their pollinators, there are various ways that people also benefit from the scents of the garden, even if we cannot always understand the messages. Smells matter to us for several reasons. One is because of their unique ability to trigger memories – this is because of the close links between the olfactory and the limbic centre of our brains. The limbic system is thought to be one of the oldest parts of our brain and relates more to subconscious reaction than to conscious action – it influences mood, memory and emotion. So powerful is this link that smells are often utilised in reminiscence therapy and to combat traumatic stress and depression – smells can bypass patterns of destructive thoughts to release more positive emotions.

Scents can also bring back memories long buried. If you have a scented plant you associate strongly with childhood or other happy times, by including it in your current garden it can add another dimension of pleasure, bringing back past memories.

Scent is also our best means of connection with nature's conversations. As we inhale the aromas of our gardens we can wonder who is talking to who and what the conversation may be. This helps remind us we are part of the natural community, not above it.

Claire Leighton writes that every season announces its arrival with a distinctive smell. She says that autumn is identified by the 'knife sharp' tang of cold and wet leaves. In many ways autumn is the richest smelling season, the smells of decay mix with the last flowers, the fruits and the storms.

What are the smells of the seasons for you?

The Victorians developed what they called the language of flowers, but this was little more than a simple code system that arbitrarily attributed specific meanings to certain flowers. More fundamentally, the smells of plants are a language, not arbitrary, but honed through millions of years of evolution to ensure that a plant can communicate whatever it needs to, whenever it needs to.

One of the greatest challenges with our sense of smell is to find the right language to describe what we are perceiving. A simple broad brush categorisation of scent describes smells in groups such as sweet, acrid, sour, floral, resinous, woody, smoky, minty or rotten. These are what Diane Ackerman calls the 'primary colours of smell'.

Of course, some things smell – just because they smell – like burning tyres or pencil shavings. However, mostly in nature smells evolve to serve a communication purpose. Like sound and colour, scent is a language that cannot function without a fluid medium to carry it, air or water usually – there can be no communication in a vacuum.

The language of scent tends to have a few set phrases:

"I'm ready and willing for sex, so come here," is typically a message from one animal to another, or from flowers to a pollinating animal. A related message is "I'm fertile and ready," or "It's time to start getting fertile,"– this is typically a message from one plant or animal to another.

This call to breed is probably the most common scent conversation in the world – all insects use it. Flowers rely on that message to call pollinators to them too; so we all depend on that message for our survival.

Another common message is "Supper's ready, safe to eat," which is often code for "Eat this and help me spread my seeds." Much of the seed distribution of plants relies on this message getting through, so we all depend on it too.

Another message that plants send to each other using scent is, "Help me, I am under attack," or "Save yourself, we are all under

33

attack." These are warnings to their neighbours to prepare their own defences.

Animals often use scent to issue a warning: "This is mine – keep out, or respect my property," and plants can communicate "I'm not safe to eat, dangerous – beware!" This is presumably a defensive message, although this is not consistent across all species – the rotting flesh smell of the Giant Arum repels us but is, presumably, delicious to the flies that pollinate it.

Having developed a sense of smell for communication, plants will sometimes use it in other ways, for example they may even smell an attacker coming, and some parasitic plants hunt down their victims by scent. As another example, fruits can smell other fruit ripening and this encourages them to ripen as well.

Plants don't seem to have one organ like a nose where the smell sensors are located – probably it is an ability that is dispersed throughout their bodies. As far as I know Darwin didn't try to hunt this down with clothes pegs.

Smells aren't always messages, but they nearly always carry information. Often smell can be used to tell when our environment changes, for example some seeds may use the 'smell' of smoke as a trigger to germinate after a fire.

The basic language of scent phrases is vastly extended in some animals who have much more sensitivity to smell and therefore scope to understand more than the norm. Some animals are able to detect disease, fitness, mood and confidence from the smell of another creature. This is the basis of new experiments using dogs and bees to detect illnesses such as cancer and diabetes, or even Covid. It has also been suggested that schizophrenia produces a detectable smell.

I once met a lady taking her completely blind dog for a walk and she described how he had a favourite route that took him past all of the smells he wanted to visit each day, to catch up with the news of the neighbourhood.

34

Some plant smells are not there for communication but come from chemicals that serve a different purpose. For example, it is not uncommon for herbs and shrubs of hot and arid countries to have internal chemicals that protect their cells from too much radiation – these chemicals act like sun lotion. It is these that give the plants their distinctive aroma and taste – rosemary, thyme, buchu and pelargoniums for example.

Plants also produce defensive chemicals as part of their immune system, to fight off attack from pests and diseases. Sometimes these defence chemicals are given the clinical sounding name of phytoncides. Phytoncides can deter fungal or herbivore attack. These also give the resiny aroma to Mediterranean shrubs like lavender, and the bitter taste to tea leaves. A common group of these chemicals are called terpenoids – you smell them in pine woods. The spicy scents of bark mulch and cut grass are terpenoids.

There is some research that suggests inhaling phytoncides can help to boost human immune systems too. Exposure to these scents is a key element of the therapeutic practice known as forest bathing.

Phytoncide molecules, like plant sunscreen chemicals, are relatively heavy and complex and buried deep within the cells, so they are mostly only released when the cells are crushed or cut. To release these aromas, especially in colder weather, we have to get close to the plants and maybe bruise the leaves, cut grass and snap conifer branches.

However, in the right conditions these defensive chemicals will volatilise into the air as aerosols where they do something that benefits everyone by becoming the nuclei on which rain condenses. Without them the rainforests would just be the forests.

Most typically in gardens the aromas we notice come from

plants that are using smells to communicate because it is those scents that have been evolved to travel, rather than stay inside the cells. Usually the communication we pick up most easily is from flower to pollinator – "Come pollinate, I have nectar for you." We also notice the message from fruits to seed distributors – "Come eat me and help spread my seed."

Much of the scent communication happening around us is something that we are completely unable to detect. The scent messages that plants use to warn each other of danger pass us by completely. Not just flowers but also roots emit chemicals that communicate with the soil creatures. The role of these root chemical messages is only beginning to be understood, but it seems to include attracting beneficial micro-organisms to help the roots, protect them from attack or help them harvest nutrients.

Like leaf tendrils, roots may taste other roots or fungi they encounter to decide whether to connect to each other. Having connected, they will help each other in various ways, including warning of drought so their neighbours can take protective measures. Direct connections can be risky as they can allow virus infections to travel too. Socially distanced communication by scent is safer.

Obviously the full palette of garden aromas do not just come from plants. Petrichor is the name of the smell of fresh rain on dry earth – this smell actually comes from a chemical called geosmin, that is produced in the soil by bacteria. Geosmin also gives the earthy smell to vegetables like beetroot. Tests have shown that humans can detect geosmin at extremely low concentrations – proof of how important it has been to our survival. By smelling geosmin we can identify water sources. Plants may not need to smell geosmin because their fine roots and fungal partners have other ways to know exactly where the water is.

Scent and taste are closely related senses. Generally detecting an airborne chemical is referred to as smell, while tasting involves picking up chemicals dissolved in water. So strictly the roots taste their surroundings rather than smell them. Plants can taste things as well as smell them. Some climbing plants will taste what their tendrils are touching to decide if it makes a good support. It is also likely that roots also taste other roots or fungi they encounter to decide whether to team up.

Plants don't always want other plants nearby. To discourage crowding they may emit repellent chemicals that stop competing plants from growing too close. This is known as allelopathy. Presumably the roots, on tasting these chemicals, decide, "No thanks, let's not grow here, we are not welcome."

Plants can feel things

As unlikely as it may seem, plants also have a sense of touch, known as thigmotropism. Touch for humans is a catch-all term for a complex sense that embodies many different facets – it encompasses the ability to perceive temperature, texture, pressure and even pain. We know that plants sense temperature and are aware that they have been wounded, but like us, do they also have more dimensions to their sense of touch?

There are at least two plants with very obvious and visible response to touch. One is the Venus Flytrap that closes when it detects that an insect is in its trap. The other is the sensitive plant – *Mimosa pudica*. This plant folds its leaves away when brushed – this behaviour probably helps them look less attractive to passing predators.

Monica Gagliano, a plant researcher in Australia, worked with this sensitive plant to demonstrate that not only can it feel touch, but it also has a memory. It can remember if it has had too many false alarms, and it then gets more relaxed about disturbance.

We also know that roots can sense when they hit an obstacle and adjust their growth accordingly. Another example of plant touch awareness is when tendrils of climbing plants change their growth in response to a suitable support – twisting to get a grip.

Although plants can sometimes detect touch, it would be hugely contentious to suggest that they can feel pain as this would need an advanced nervous system. However, we know for sure that trees and other plants are aware that they have been wounded and attacked. We know this because we see that they respond in various ways to mobilise their own immune system. For example, the wounded tissue will send a signal to nearby cells that respond appropriately and the cells around a point of infection sometimes sacrifice themselves to form a barrier against the spread of the disease.

In response to attack the plant often makes more of their natural defence compounds. Also they can send out warning signals to other plants nearby to get their own defences ready. So plants have an advanced awareness of being attacked and they rely on it often.

When we think of our own senses the word proprioception rarely springs to mind. We are accustomed to think in terms of the dominant four or five; sight, hearing, smell, etc. Yet researchers believe that we have many more senses – 9 at least but maybe up to 53.

Related to balance, the sense of proprioception is our ability to orient in space, to know which way up we are and where our limbs are positioned. It is how we can sit on a chair without miscalculating our position, how we can pick our keys up from the floor, and it is how we know our backside from our elbow. In plants this sense is usually referred to as gravitropism – the ability of a plant to adjust growth in response to the direction of gravity – and while they may not have a complex spatial awareness, they do at least know their up from their down.

The mechanism is believed to involve starch granules called statoliths that are held in membranes in the root tips. The granules move in response to gravity and the plant detects what happens to them, and as a result shoots know to go up and roots know to go down.

Researchers have also explored how plants respond to zero gravity in space. They were surprised to learn that many can adapt. Apparently, plants can substitute light gradient cues for orientation when gravity does not work. This shows that plants do not just have senses but they are able to adapt to unknown circumstances. However, if deprived of all sources of orientation information, the space plants do get confused and grow in random directions.

Recent research has also shown that sometimes plants may, in fact, have a much finer sense of spatial positioning than botanists have ever recognised. It has recently been found that after damage, flowers and petals readjust to get back to the perfect position for their pollinators to land safely. We really didn't know this before. There are always new wonders to discover, even on the much-trodden earth just outside our doors.

Shhh – they can hear you

Recently scientists have discovered another amazing thing. Plants can sometimes hear things and respond accordingly. This is not to do with people, even Princes, talking to them, or about them liking classical music, it is about them detecting things they need to hear to aid their survival. Listening to music or people chuntering on would not do this.

Recent research has shown that some flowers can use 'hearing' to tell when pollinators are approaching – the flowers 'hear the buzz' and produce more nectar in response. Imagine the fun Darwin could have had with earplugs, had he known.

There are even some studies that suggest plants use the sound of chewing or approaching insects as a signal to build up their defences. These responses to sound have clear survival benefit.

The full soundscape of the garden may have limited significance to plants, but without doubt it is an essential part of our own garden experience. The study of the impact of natural sounds on our wellbeing is less advanced than studies of visual contemplation, but researchers have identified that some sounds produce a similar relaxation-state as meditation.

Much of the richness of our garden soundscape comes from the sounds that plants make. Psithurism is the word for the sound of rustling leaves. The word comes from the Greek root, psithuros, which means 'whispering, slanderous'. Are the trees whispering about us as they rustle? (Are they sniggering – "Check out the lockdown hair!")

Another whispering word is susurrous, which refers to whispering or rustling in general, with less intonations of malevolent gossip. The word susurration comes from this root and means the sound of wind in trees.

Thomas Hardy wrote that by listening to the way different trees rustle we should be able to determine what species are growing nearby. Gertude Jekyll, the Victorian garden designer, also wrote of how she trained and sharpened her senses to better perceive what was going on in her garden. She claimed that she could tell by the rustling in grass if it was a bird, lizard, mouse or snake passing by. She even claimed she could identify birds by the sound of their flight. No surprise, therefore, that she was a master of identifying the source of a susurration.

She wrote:

The Birches have a small, quick, high pitched sound; so near that of falling rain I am often deceived into thinking it really is rain, when it is only their leaves hitting each other with a rain-like

40

patter. The voice of the Oak leaves is also rather high pitched, though lower than that of the Birch. Chestnut leaves in a mild breeze sound much more deliberate; a sort of slow slither.

I confess to a distinct dislike of Poplars rustling; feeling it to be painfully fussy, unrestful, disturbing. On the other hand, how soothing and delightful is the murmur of Scotch Firs, both near and far. And what pleasant, muffled music is that of a wind-waved field of corn, and especially ripe Barley.

There are many plants that will contribute to the susurration orchestra of your garden. Despite the reservations of Gertrude Jekyll, Quaking Aspen is, in my view, a vital part of our soundscape. It produces a shimmering whisper in every breeze that can be a delightful counterpoint to the visual sparkling of the leaves. Unfortunately, this is a large tree and unsuitable for small plots, but you may have one growing nearby that you can enjoy while walking.

Manageable whispering plants for smaller gardens include tall grasses such as Miscanthus, also known as Silver Grasses. These produce dense clumps with feathery flower heads. Emerging late summer, they arch gracefully under their own weight and stay attractive even until winter. They dance and hiss in the strengthening breezes of autumn.

Another important part of the garden soundscape is the sound of water. Doubtless we evolved to be alert for sounds of water, just as we had to pick up smell, as essential for survival. The sound of gentle water running or falling, is proven to be calming, whether just raindrops in puddles, fountains, or more subtle artificial features like the Japanese deer scarers.

The rain symphony
Although there is not a word for it, raindrops also make different sounds when falling on leaves of different shapes and textures. Leaves collect fine rain or mist allowing the water to gather into

larger droplets. Small soft and furry leaves send small quiet drops through to the ground. Large leathery leaves, especially with extended tips, allow large drops to form before they fall with an audible patter. Each tree therefore creates a music of its own drops falling to the ground in a pattern or rhythm that is quite unique to that individual.

The songsters

Birds and their songs are such a vital part of our auditory landscape that we named them for it – the songbirds. Michael McCarthy argues that songs are important gifts of the birds to us – listen up, listen sideways and listen down, you will hear a rich and complex soundscape. Birds have a structure called the syrinx that consists of cartilage and two membranes that vibrate with airflow at superfast speeds – one on each side of the syrinx – to create two independent sources of sound. This has given them an ability to vocalise that is almost unmatched in the animal kingdom.

Birds call as well as sing. Scientists believe that call sounds are innate and instinctive, rather like the bark of a dog or the meow of a cat. Songs, however, are much more complex and require much more subtle and prolonged vocalisations. There is research evidence that young birds have to learn their songs through imitation and practice, much like humans learn language – following careful listening and memorisation, there must be practice, emulation and repetition. Very young birds first practice what is known as a 'subsong', much like a human baby's first speech attempts.

Some bird species have greater vocalisation skills than others – these are the birds that develop the most complex songs and may have mimicry skills reproducing sounds of non-bird origin. Since bird calls and songs play an important role in their survival and social bonding, they have to ensure that they can be heard. Researchers believe that a reason that birds perch on high structures is not just for visual scrutiny of their surroundings, but also to give a good vantage for vocalising.

Birds will adjust their songs to their favoured habitats. Birds of low woodland cover tend to vocalise in lower tones than those that perch on high. Similarly, it has been found that the dawn chorus is timed before competing noises build up. Birds near noisy places, airports, railway lines or roads begin to sing earlier and with a different pitch. Many studies have linked natural sounds of diverse birdsong and the sound of susurration to reduced stress.

Listening in on bird and insect song is not just relaxing, but it is also a window into another complex and rich dimension of nature's ongoing conversation. Another proven relaxing sound is the gentle chirp of the cricket. Crickets are grass feeders so their soundscape too is woven by plants out of a colourless gas.

Good plants to grow for songsters

Few people realise that plants are the foundation for the music of the garden, yet they are, just as for scent and beauty too. All these things are woven for us by photosynthesis. By careful plant selection you can grow and enrich your garden soundscape, and it will enrich you too. Obviously a good starting point is to choose plants that are good at attracting birds. Even birds that generally prefer insects, will eat fruits and berries to vary their diet and to extend their feeding season.

Birds also like trees with good vantage and nesting potential. Older trees with cavities attract specialists like woodpeckers, whose hammering adds a new dimension to the garden symphony. Often any berry producing shrub or tree will be popular additions to the diet of songbirds, but some are particularly worth including in your garden, to get the best soundscape possible.

We can also add to the soundscape of the garden by considering which plants are good for attracting insects. This is, of course, good for birds too. Fortunately, most flowering plants are designed for attracting pollinating insects as their survival depends on this, but some are especially effective. We should also remember the insects that are leaf-feeders more than pollinators, but also are important sound-makers, such as crickets. Fortunately, crickets are not fussy eaters – they can survive on a range of plants, including weeds, seeds and small fruits. They may also eat rotting vegetation.

Good plants for birds are:

Mahonia. Mahonias are evergreen shrubs with fragrant yellow flowers, often in winter or very early spring – so invaluable for early insects. Later in the year, dark blue berries appear, earning its common name of Oregon Grape. Birds enjoy the berries so this plant has many assets that support diversity in your garden.

Snowy Mespilus. Some fruit and bird associations are so reliable that a chorus is almost guaranteed. The berries of Snowy Mespilus, *Amelanchier canadensis*, are amongst the earliest to ripen in late summer and Blackbirds absolutely adore them.

Holly. Although Holly berries may be ripe by autumn, birds don't usually feed on them until late winter when other food is scarce. Only female Holly plants produce berries, but there must be a male nearby to ensure pollination. To get abundant fruit on a Holly requires a large well-established tree and few small gardens can afford the space. Other berry producing plants are arguably more reliable and more manageable.

Ivy. In autumn, Ivy flowers attract many insects, especially the drone flies or the Ivy bee, one of the last bees to fly before winter hibernation. These in turn provide food for Robins and Wrens, who may shelter overwinter in the dense cover that Ivy provides. When the black Ivy berries appear, other food is scarce, so they are devoured by many birds, from Thrushes, Waxwings, Starlings and Jays, to Finches and Blackbirds. Ivy leaves also provide food for caterpillars of the Holly Blue butterfly, a piece of summer sky fallen to earth that sparkles amidst the flowers in July, it could not be more different from the skies that oversaw its birth.

Hawthorn. The leaves of Hawthorn are the food-plant for caterpillars of many species of moth, providing food for baby birds in spring. Hawthorn is another all-rounder that is a boost for garden diversity. Clusters of haws may stay on Hawthorn trees until February or March. They are the favourite berry of Blackbirds, Redwings and Fieldfares and are enjoyed by many other birds too, including Chaffinches, Starlings and Greenfinches.

Honeysuckle. In summer, the scented flowers of climbing Honeysuckle attract many insects and so provide food for a different range of birds. In autumn, the plant also provides berries and the tangled stems give winter shelter for birds such as Thrushes, Warblers and Bullfinches.

Rowan or Mountain Ash (*Sorbus aucuparia*) is another dependable, attractive berrying tree that includes varieties suitable for small gardens. Depending on which variety you choose, it will bear red, yellow or white berries from late August to October.

Cotoneaster. Shrub or small tree Cotoneasters carry small red berries from autumn onwards. These plants are often the first to be stripped as the berries are extremely popular with Blackbirds, Thrushes and Waxwings.

Guelder Rose. The native deciduous shrub, *Viburnum opulus*, known as Guelder Rose, bears heavy clusters of glossy berries in yellow or red varieties, from November through to March. These are loved by Mistle Thrushes and Bullfinches, in particular.

Roses. Rose hips are also eaten by many birds. The largest hips are produced by *Rosa rugosa*. Although bulky, tough and dry, these are taken by Blackbirds, Fieldfares and Mistle Thrushes. The smaller hips of the Dog Rose *Rosa canina*, are eaten by a wider range of birds and can stay edible until late winter.

Buddleia is not called the Butterfly Bush for no reason. Simon Barnes refers to it as a summoning bush – just plant it and butterflies will appear, guaranteed. Of course, butterflies mean caterpillars which are essential for chick rearing.

If the common Buddleia is too big or aggressive for a small garden, there are smaller varieties such as the lovely, graceful Buddleia 'Lochinch' and recently the 'Buzz' collection bred for containers.

Lavender. During its flowering period, Lavender is buzzing with insect visitors. It has a long flowering season and many other features that merit its presence in the garden. There is an extraordinary range of varieties to choose from and one of my favourites is French Lavender (*Lavandula stoechas*) which flowers in our garden until the frost calls it to a halt.

Teasels are wildflowers that form striking seed heads in early autumn which can last until December, depending on the weather. Goldfinches, Sparrows and Buntings all love Teasel seed.

Sunflower. If the flowers on large flowered annual Sunflowers are left to form seed heads they provide food throughout autumn for Finches, Long-tailed Tits, Nuthatches and other seed-eating birds.

The first flowers

Finding flowers like these for insects in high summer is not a challenge. A little more difficult – and especially important to maintain a healthy insect population – are those plants that flower in the 'shoulder' seasons, early spring and late autumn, when few other flowers are around.

Early spring bulbs like Aconites, Snowdrops Anemone and Crocus are lifelines for the first emerging insects of the year. Also amongst the first to flower are the catkins of shrubby Willows – although wind pollinated, their pollen is important for the first emerging insects of spring.

The late flowers

After the summer flush of flowers is fading, late autumn flowers can be obtained from Asters, also known as Michaelmas Daisy, and Goldenrod, both of the Daisy family. Also invaluable are Sedums – the ice plants are hardy fleshy succulents with flowers adored by the last butterflies of the season. *Schizostylis*, a plant from South Africa with vivid pink or white flowers that seem almost too exotic for our climate, proves tough enough to flower in our gardens from September until winter.

The winter flowers, the most unlikely of all

It may seem surprising that some plants flower in winter at all – why expend the energy when sunlight is so scarce? Like night flowering, this is primarily a strategy to avoid intense competition for pollinator visits.

In winter there are fewer pollinators active but rarely are there none at all (except in the very worst weather). Some moths do not hibernate or migrate as most insects do. In the UK, the Winter Moth, the December Moth and Spring Usher tough it out and remain active. Even some bees may be awake too. Honey bees sometimes leave the hive on mild winter days to eliminate waste, and they will not turn down a meal if they find one. Buff-tailed bumblebees (*Bumbus terrestris*) also frequently fly on mild winter days and make use of the winter flowering plants they find (I saw one feeding in my garden on Christmas Day). Those plants that dare to flower in the winter can expect to get the attention of these insects all to themselves. In doing so they play an important role of keeping the pollinators alive through the hard times.

Weatherproofing

To survive and to be able to flower in the winter, plants have evolved certain qualities in their flowers. Large flamboyant petals will be destroyed by frost, so winter flowers are more typically small, hard and waxy, nestled in the shelter of leaves and stems. Often they also come in long succession so that new blooms replace those that are lost, giving a long flowering season.

Because, like night flowers, they rely less on show and flower colour to attract their pollinators, a high proportion of winter flowering plants produce scent that travels widely to reach the active insects, wherever they may be. Just a few of these plants can produce a great scent sensation in the garden.

Margery Fish wrote of her love of cutting sprigs of the unusual winter flowering plants in her garden, to scent the house, but especially so that she could closely inspect and get to know the curious beauty of their tiny and unusual flowers.

Winter flowering plants are essential to the hardy insects; here are some of the most important:

Winter Honeysuckle. *Lonicera fragrantissima* and *Lonicera x purpusii* are both known as Winter Honeysuckles. Unlike their summer flowering relatives in the Honeysuckle family, the Winter Honeysuckles do not climb, but make straggly and scruffy shrubs.

48

Yet despite this there is great value in the mass of tiny cream-coloured winter flowers hidden amongst tangled stems because just one bush can fill an entire garden with fragrance.

Winter Camellias. Some flowering shrubs that we normally associate with spring come in varieties that are so precocious that their flowers may even appear in December. Of the Camellia varieties, those that have been bred from the species *Camellia sasanqua* often produce winter flower, as do those bred from *Camellia oliviae*, with the added advantage that they are scented. Hybrids that have blood from these species betray their winter flowering habit by their names. Good ones to look for are:

Camellia 'Winter Joy'
Camellia 'Yuletide'
Camellia 'Cornish Snow'

Winter Viburnum. And then there is another, more striking member of the winter active plants, *Viburnum bodnantense* 'Dawn'. This is a large deciduous shrub of upright growth, with dark green, ovate leaves and clusters of scented, light pink and white flowers opening from red buds. The flowers appear in autumn through to spring.

Daphnes are a group of small shrubs, usually evergreen and scented, all with a tendency for winter flowers. They are excellent for filling neglected corners or giving low cover in a mixed shrub border. These are the Daphnes that you are likely to encounter:

Daphne bholua makes a rounded medium sized shrub with intense pink scented flowers, the cultivar 'Jaqueline Postill' is the most sought-after variety, it flowers in late winter.

Daphne cneorum is a spreading evergreen with scented pink flowers in early spring.

Also valuable is *Daphne odora*, which is a slightly shorter plant, also evergreen, with flowers of a paler pink in spring.

Daphne laureola, our native Spurge Laurel is a dark leaved evergreen that tolerates heavy shade. It grows to about a metre and produces small green/yellow scented flowers in late winter.

Unlike many in its family, the shrub, *Daphne mezereum* is deciduous. It produces scented pink flowers along its stiff upright stems from late winter to early spring.

If you have the room there are also much larger shrubs or even trees to choose from:

Elaeagnus pungens is a large evergreen shrub that produces tiny well-scented flowers in November. The standard form is somewhat undistinguished but variegated varieties are beautiful, fast-growing, and great for cutting, although possibly too large for many gardens. The variety 'Maculata' is the most common form found in nurseries and has bold golden splashes on the leaves that bring a cheer to any dark corner. 'Goldrim' has yellow edged leaves.

Winter Cherry. For me, the star of the show is the winter flowering cherry, *Prunus subhirtella* 'Autumnalis'. In mild years the flowers can open at the first hint of the approach of the winter season and continue through to spring. It is beautiful, not just because of its early flowering, but also because of its gentle elegance. The pretty, pale pink flowers are small and sprinkle the branches like a soft snow flurry caught in dawn light. Overall this winter variety is much more subtle than the overpowering pink explosions of its main season cousins.

Glastonbury Thorn. Closely related to Cherry is the Hawthorn. The native Hawthorn, *Crataegus monogyna*, has a peculiar variety

'Biflora' that flowers in winter and again in spring. This variety is also known as the Glastonbury Thorn, since the original tree from which the rest are propagated grew in Glastonbury and like the town it has attracted much folklore around itself. One legend has it that the tree grew from the staff of Joseph of Arimathea who was said to have fled to Glastonbury with the holy grail. Regardless of the mythology, the tree certainly has attracted strong feelings through history, the original has been attacked and vandalised several times, including by the roundhead soldiers in the civil war.

Sweet Box. *Sarcococca ruscifolia* is a small evergreen bush also known as Sweet Box. It makes a small neat glossy evergreen with white spidery sweet-smelling flowers that sprout along the length of the stem through early winter.

Coronilla. Bright dots of unseasonal sunny colour can come from *Coronilla glauca*, a small shrub of the pea family. It has slightly fleshy grey green leaves and clusters of yellow flowers; very typical of the family, they come with a lovely scent. If sheltered and in mild weather it can flower through the year end until spring, only resting to catch breath before starting again.

Hamamelis. Witch Hazels, *Hamamelis mollis*, are worth a space in many gardens because of their year-round interest. They make shapely shrubs, have leaves reminiscent of Hazel and often with attractive autumn colour. After the leaves fall, the stems are dotted with a long succession of unusual spidery, sweetly-scented flowers in shades of yellow to orange – very striking against a dark backdrop. There is a related species, *Hamamelis virginiana*, that originates in America where it has the common name of 'Winterbloom'.

Winter sweet. Despite its name, the Winter Sweet, *Chimonanthus fragrans*, actually has more of a spicy than a sweet scent. It also produces pale yellow bell-shaped flowers along the bare stems in winter. They are larger than Witch Hazel but no less curious. The leaves also have a spicy scent. It can take a while after planting to start to flower, but once established it is perfect for a sheltered spot that you often walk by so that you can enjoy the beauty and the smell.

Gorse. It is not just exotic garden plants that dare the winter, our native wild plants sometimes do as well. We have already met the Spurge Laurel. In addition, Gorse, *Ulex europaeus*, is renowned for producing a continued light scattering of bright yellow, scented flowers through the year, giving rise to the saying 'when Gorse stops flowering, kissing will go out of fashion'. For an undistinguished looking shrub, it may be surprising that Gorse has one of the best scents you can find in the garden – a mix of vanilla and coconut, with citrus undertones. Although it is technically true that Gorse flowers through the year, winter flowering is intermittent at best, with some individuals very shy and others quite prolific. As far as I know no one has selected a variety for reliable winter flowers.

Cornus mas. Although it is not scented it is also worth considering *Cornus mas*, the Cornelian Cherry, as it dots its stems with small yellow flowers in winter, sometimes followed by red berries, providing support for pollinators and birds too.

Seeing plants for what they are

I hope this is helping you look at the plants outside your window with a different perspective. Researchers continue to demonstrate in ever more detail how, although plants do things differently and at a very different pace, they actually have more in common with us than we have ever understood. Our understanding of the good things they weave for us is growing too – they bring us colour, sound, movement and health, and a great conversation.

Before we leave them to their world weaving, I would now like to dig deeper into how plants work, by looking at their structure.

Trunks and stems

The stems are obviously the body of the plants, they hold the leaves in the air to feed in sunlight and catch the passing breezes. Inside the stem are two vascular circulatory systems, like our blood system. One of these is called the phloem; it carries sugars and other carbohydrates down from the leaves where they are made, and around the plant to feed the growth of roots, stems and flowers and to storage organs for future use – whatever is needed, wherever it is needed. A second circulatory system called the xylem grows through the stem also. This brings water and dissolved minerals from the roots, transporting them up through the plant – whatever is needed, wherever it is needed.

In woody plants the phloem forms in an outer cylinder below the bark, known as sapwood, where the sap moves; the xylem is deeper, further inside and as xylem cells die they harden and become the solid, fibrous woody 'heartwood' where nothing moves anymore. When we fell a tree the timber we use is made of this heartwood.

Meristems the regenerators

The shoot tips, root tips and outer bark all contain what are known as meristem cells. These are undifferentiated cells, as are human stem cells. These are critical cells for plant growth and development. They have not specialised for a particular function but are key to the plant's modular growth. They contain the potential to become anything – flower, leaf, fruit, whatever is needed, whenever it is needed. They can therefore replace or regrow anything that gets destroyed or eaten.

Meristems repair damage and compensate for failed or unbalanced growth. They can even regrow the entire plant from a fragment. This ability to regrow from parts is the basis of 'asexual propagation', that allows plants to produce new individuals from offshoots and enables us to propagate plants from cuttings. It is also why some plants are such rapidly spreading weeds – Bindweeds, for example, can produce dozens of new plants from tiny pieces of root split from the parent as we try to pull them up. It is also the reason why trees can continue to grow in ever increasing and more complex forms.

Leaves, solar panels and more

An important function of the stem is to raise the leaves into the light. The leaves are the solar panels. In most plants, the place where photosynthesis happens is the leaves – the key molecule that does this work is called chlorophyll and is what gives the leaves their green colour. As more evidence of our common ancestry, it is interesting to note that chlorophyll and haemoglobin are similar in their makeup – the main difference is that chlorophyll is built around magnesium rather than the iron in haemoglobin. The chlorophyll absorbs mostly blue and red light and reflects green light – hence the colour we see.

Leaves absorb carbon dioxide and exhale oxygen, the reverse of animal respiration and at the heart of our mutual dependency. To allow carbon dioxide in and oxygen out the leaves have tiny pores for breathing, called stomata, each guarded by special cells that can open and close, to breathe in and out. Inevitably these pores also allow water to escape as vapour – this causes a pressure deficit in the stem that pulls more water from the soil into the roots and up the plant. The stomata are finely tuned. In dry conditions they open less widely to reduce water loss and in very dry conditions the plant may switch to do most of its breathing at night; they can store what they take in until the following day.

Leaves are remarkable things – they are the food manufacture hubs and also, in some sense, the lungs for breathing, and in a way they are the 'heart' that moves fluid through the plant. They can also be 'hands' and tasting organs too. Adapted leaves form the tendrils used by climbing plants and often they feel their way looking for an appropriate support. Leaves can also be places where food is stored, that's why the thick leaves of the cabbage family such as Kale, Spinach and Chard are so nutritious for us too.

Many of these leafy vegetables are believed to have originally evolved near to the sea as the thick waxiness protects the leaves from salt damage. Not far from where I am sitting is one of the few remaining colonies of wild cabbage in Britain, clinging to a cliff looking more like a farm escape than the distinguished ancestor of our staple winter food.

Why do some plants lose their leaves?

An important way that plants adapt to different places is shown by their leaf persistence. The key difference is between those that keep their leaves through the year – evergreens – and those that lose them in the autumn – deciduous. Having invested energy and resources in making a leaf it surely makes sense to get the longest use possible out of it? So why do some plants lose them?

Deciduous trees evolve and dominate in climates and regions where the risk of keeping a leaf through the winter outweighs the advantages. What could these risks be? Well, although we think of hot dry weather as when we lose most water, cold and windy days can be very dehydrating too. Dropping leaves in winter is a way to reduce moisture loss – moisture that can be hard to replace if the ground is frozen. Keeping leaves in winter also increases the risk of blowing over and of catching disease.

So, the plants that do keep their leaves through winter in cold climates, especially the taller ones, need special adaptations. Nearly all cold climate evergreens have waxy coatings on the leaves to reduce moisture loss. Many also have very small leaves or needles to reduce the surface area, also reducing wind resistance and disease risk. Typically evergreens also have defences that reduce the likelihood of the leaves being eaten – they may carry thorns or prickles, like Holly, or may contain bitter and off-putting chemicals or even poisons as the Yew tree does. You can detect these defences by crushing the leaves and smelling – the rich incense scents of conifers, Eucalyptus, Bay, Thyme and Rosemary are there to deter browsing animals. Please don't try the Yew leaves.

Actually the term 'evergreen' is misleading, as all leaves fall eventually but evergreens let them go slowly one by one, only replacing a leaf as the old one gets worn out by use. A notable exception is the Maidenhair tree – *Ginkgo biloba*. This is an extraordinary tree, the only surviving species of a very ancient family, neither conifer nor broadleaf, it is one of the oldest known tree species on the earth. The tree has an unusual habit of dropping all its leaves together in autumn after they have turned a beautiful golden yellow. Probably this is also a strategy to avoid winter moisture loss or wind damage. Whatever the reason, the result is one of the greatest spectacles in nature – suddenly, when the tree feels the time has come (often cued by the first hard frost), the ground beneath transforms to a yellow sea of leaves.

Leaves of all shapes and sizes
Have you ever wondered why leaves have such different shapes and sizes?

Every living thing that shares our gardens reveals its evolutionary history in its behaviour. Scientists believe that the factors that have most impact on leaf size are water availability and climate. If there is no reason not to, plants let their leaves get as big as possible to harvest more light and air. That is why plants in tropical forests tend to have larger leaves. But bigger leaves will lose moisture more easily, so water availability limits their maximum size. Bigger, softer leaves can also overheat in high temperatures, suffer cold damage too easily and tear and tatter in high winds.

Plants that need to cope with hard weather and climate stresses therefore tend to have smaller leaves. The balance of stress and opportunity a given plant species has evolved to cope with, will have determined its typical leaf size, from the big lush expanses of bananas to the tight rolled needles of conifers.

The great falling into autumn colour

Many gardeners treasure the moments of transient beauty that grace us as the wheel of the year turns. One of the most important of these is the falling of the leaves.

Gradually, through the busy spring and summer, the constant work of the leaves takes a toll, the chlorophyll loses efficiency and they begin to look tired. The plant begins its preparations for autumn and winter. Part of this preparation is recycling – tired chlorophyll is broken down and used to help build food stores for a long, hungry winter hibernation ahead.

Green chlorophyll is not the only coloured pigment that leaves contain, but during the time of active photosynthesis, it masks the other pigments – so the leaves look green. After use, the chlorophylls break down into colourless compounds, allowing the otherwise hidden pigments of yellow xanthophylls and orange beta-carotene to be revealed. These pigments are present throughout the year but not visible to us.

57

In contrast, ageing leaves manufacture red pigments (anthocyanins) once roughly half of the chlorophyll has been recycled. It is believed that they may give the leaf a final protection against stress or insect attack. Insects seem to favour yellow leaves and avoid the reds and this gives the plants more time to reclaim leaf nutrients for use next year. Anthocyanin pigments appear red to blue, according to pH. They occur in all tissues of plants, providing colour in leaves, stems, roots, flowers, and fruits. They are most visible in the petals of many flowers.

The recycled resources released from breakdown of old leaves are stored in the tree's roots, branches, stems, and trunk until next summer when they are called upon to re-leaf the tree. Then, as the plant senses falling temperatures, it forms what is known as an abscission layer between the leaf and stem; this disconnects the leaf from further nutrient flow in either direction. Then the time comes to finally let go – the abscission layer is the point of breakage of old attachments. Leaves do not just fall, they are actively let go of. Before they go they may have a chance to blaze in brilliant colours. Some get to go on unexpected adventures, collected as treasures in the pocket of a nature-seeking forager.

Again this is when the different sizes and shapes of leaves have an influence. Each leaf has a distinctive journey to the ground, some spiral, pirouette, swoop and glide in arcs, some drop leadenly. Whichever way it falls, leaving its parent plant is not really the end of the leaf's story.

Falling leaves are perhaps the last gift that deciduous trees give us in the autumn – spiralling through the sky in rainbow hues, each unique in colour, texture and final dance, they are a flourish of delight to cherish as the nights begin to darken.

All parts of a tree sustain other beings, this is true in death as in life. Leaves join the soil where worms and fungi digest them and create humus, releasing nutrients for the parents and other plants; even better, acids released from the decaying organic matter in turn release more nutrients from soil minerals.

Fallen leaves are also an important habitat – they provide vital winter shelter for insects and small mammals like hedgehogs. They are also essential kicking material. Leaves belong back in the soil where they came from. So, let's forsake the rakes and leaf blowers and enjoy the cycle and the spectacle.

Paying attention to the beauty of change – Momijigari
Fleeting changes in nature as the year progresses add much to life's beauty. Remember to allow the transient wonders to add to your delight. The transient beauty of the changing leaves is celebrated in the Japanese tradition of momijigari. Momijigari means 'red leaf hunting' and is the term used to describe autumn leaf viewing. For Buddhists, the experience is a reminder that life is fleeting.

Puddles are another transient garden beauty that should not be underestimated – they are great for contemplation, appearing either shallow or infinitely deep. They can be fantastic starting points for story making – 'What lies through the gateway?' Also puddles give us the gift of mirrors dotted through the landscape – superb for photography or painting inspiration.

Flower power

Having talked about the core functional parts of the plant – the stems and leaves – what about the showstoppers, the flowers. To really understand flowers, we should remember that they were not evolved for us but for insects, the fact we love them too is just a happy bonus.

Flowers hold the plant's reproductive organs. Because plants cannot move to their mate, they have developed an ingenious system for reproduction – to be so dazzling and alluring that animals rush to them and do their bidding. For reproduction, the male 'sperm', the pollen, is carried to the female by insects or other animals that are attracted to their reward, usually nectar, hidden in the flowers. This reward is made more desirable because it comes together with beauty and intoxicating scent.

Flower colours and shapes evolved to direct the insects to their reward. Because insects see different colours than humans do, the flowers may look totally different to them than to us. If we photograph flowers with cameras that can capture UV light, we see them more like insects do. We find that they have patterns we cannot usually see and these are sometimes referred to as landing strips that point to the nectar and pollen.

Different flowers for different pollinators

Perhaps the most significant distinguishing feature of pollinating insects is between those that have long tongues compared to more simple mouths. Only long tongued insects – honey and bumble bees, moths or butterflies – can feed from tubular flowers like Foxglove, Honeysuckle or Aquilegia. Pollinators with short tongues, like hoverflies and small bees, need simpler more open flowers like Daisies.

Sometimes we carry the stamp of history, wherever we go. If you have Aquilegias (columbines) in your garden are they compact or do they have long spurs? The very longest spurs are inherited from strains that originated in the USA where long tongued pollinators such as Hummingbirds and Hawkmoths are more common. European strains tend to have more compact spurs that suit bees and other small insects.

As part of a garden observation experiment you can plant patches of flowers of different shapes and colours and watch who comes for tea in each patch – orchestrate your experience of pollinators as well as the plants. Remember it is not just flying insects that pollinate – beetles and ladybugs do too – the small size of these creatures mean that they can access small dense flowers closed to larger bees.

There is a story of Charles Darwin that illustrates how the co-evolution of flowers and pollinators helped him to refine his theories of evolution. In 1862, an Orchid grower sent Darwin a collection of Orchids from Madagascar, which included an Orchid, *Angraecum sesquipedale*, that has an exceptionally long tubular nectary (approaching 30cm) and in a book on Orchid pollination, Darwin predicted that this extreme shape could only have evolved alongside a moth with an exceptionally long tongue to pollinate it, otherwise the Orchid would not survive. It was not until 130 years later that the right moth was finally confirmed feeding on the Orchid.

As the seasons progress, so there are changes in the most prevalent and most effective pollinators. The flowers are adapted to be in sync. That is why we see waves of changing colour and flower form in wild plants to best suit the preferences of their most abundant partners.

The structure of flowers

As I wrote this heading, I could almost hear the groans. Anyone who studied biology at school may have heard more about flower structure than they care to know; revealing how our school curriculum often confuses the naming of things with the understanding of things. Leave the styles, stamens and pistils in the textbooks for now. Essentially there are only a few key elements to flowers that the plant has to get right.

The primary job of flowers is to be pollinated, so the reproductive parts are carefully positioned on the insect's route to its rewards. The male pollen and the female receptor are both produced where the insect must brush past. The next most important job a flower must do is call attention and summon the pollinators – the petals, colours and aromas are there to do this. Thirdly, it is vital for the flower that the pollinator can land safely and be guided to the centre even in wind and rain. Many petals are shaped and positioned to provide just the right stable landing spot.

After pollination there must be rewards. To encourage the pollinators to return and to help them survive in the meantime, flowers bestow gifts. The gifts are often food. This food is usually nectar and often a share of the pollen that many insects eat. Sometimes the petals are also nibbled too.

Another gift is shelter. Flowers can be a safe place to shelter from the weather and hide from predators. Lacewing Flies, Ladybug beetles and Earwigs are beneficial creatures that, although small, can consume a great number of garden pests – aphids, thrips and Whitefly amongst them. These insects need shelter and they like hollow stems, or dense ground litter, but they will also often choose flower heads as their safe places. Bees often sleep nestled deep in flowers. Research has shown that the temperature inside flowers is often much higher than outside.

Flower colours

Flower colours come from pigments produced in the tissue of the petals. Primarily the colour is there to catch the attention of pollinators, but it may serve other purposes too. Do you remember when in pre-Covid days holidays overseas were possible? Was your impression that the flower colours were brighter than they were at home? Researchers have found that this is not just a trick of the light. Flowers actually can be more intensely coloured in hotter drier climates, because the flowers produce more pigments as sunscreen for their fragile tissues. The leaves of herbs are more richly scented in hot dry countries, for the same reason, to reduce overheating. The plants produce less carbohydrates and instead produce more oils, the oils deter herbivores, act as sunscreen and even have a cooling effect.

Unnatural shapes

In a never-ending quest for novelty, humans have bred or selected plants that have flowers of such dense and complex shapes that the reproductive parts are difficult for pollinators to reach. Old-fashioned Roses are examples – these mutations would have quickly died out in nature but we keep them alive for our fascination.

Whilst some wildlife may still benefit from these over-complex flowers – they are great for sheltering, making nests and feeding unobserved for example – generally, to support the most pollinators, we should favour simple flowers in our gardens. Once the flowers are fertilised, energy goes to seed production – job done, the flowers can slowly fade away. The transient nature of blossom is partly what makes it precious.

In Japan, traditions have developed over centuries that celebrate transient beauty. Wabi-sabi is the Japanese term for the beauty and poignancy of transience. Leonard Koren, in his book *Wabi-Sabi: for Artists, Designers, Poets & Philosophers*, describes it this way:

> 'Wabi-sabi is the beauty of things imperfect, impermanent, and incomplete, the antithesis of our Western notion of beauty as something perfect, enduring, and monumental.'

Hanami 'flower viewing' is the Japanese traditional custom of gathering to view and enjoy the transient beauty of flowers, ('hana') refers typically to the blossoms of Cherry trees ('sakura') or, Plum ('ume') trees. For a short time, a cloud of colour engulfs the entire tree. Then, all too quickly, the spectacle fades and petal confetti falls to line the streets.

In other regions of the world where wildflowers produce seasonal spectacles, such as South Africa, flower tourism is becoming popular. In Cornwall, many grand gardens and estates have festival days oriented to viewing mass displays of Bluebells or Snowdrops.

Other ways to pollinate

Not every plant follows the same flowering strategy. Some even forsake animal pollination entirely and use wind to do the work of carrying pollen for them. Often, these produce their male flowers as catkins that emit clouds of pollen – on mild slightly windy days you may see it floating off in clouds of pale yellow – each minute speck the beginnings of a future tree.

These wind-pollinated flowers do not need the colours and scents of petals, but they are no less carefully constructed. Analysis of the form of some flower structures, especially conifer cones, shows that they are precisely fashioned to create small air vortices that deliver the flying pollen to exactly where the female receptors are. Since breezes are more reliable in early spring than insects are, many of the very earliest flowers are wind pollinated – the soft yellow puffs of Willow catkins amongst them. Although they need not invest in nectar, the pollen that these flowers produce can be a lifeline for early emerging insects.

Flower hunters

Some flowers have evolved to do a very different job entirely, instead of pollination they are hunters catching prey for digestion. Amongst the carnivorous plants, the sundews, flytraps and the pitcher plants all use their flowers as weapons. These have all evolved in places with very infertile soils so they need the extra nutrients that insect prey gives them.

Tiny flower ancestors

The tiniest plants, the mosses and lichens that hug the earth and bark, do not have flowers but their reproductive organs, known as antheridia, produce sperm-like cells called antherizoids that swim through water films and in raindrops to find nearby egg cells. Although mosses can survive dry weather, they need wet weather to reproduce. Once fertilised, rather than seeds, mosses and ferns produce minute spores that can travel miles in the wind. Spores are highly mobile but carry no food reserves with them – on arrival they have a precarious existence until they gradually get to a sufficient size to gather resources.

Producing a grand mass of flowers and seed uses lots of resources. To get the strength to do this, a large flowering plant needs fertile well-watered soil and good light. That is why plants with large showy flowers are associated with fertile habitats, whilst mosses and ferns can get by in dry and infertile places.

Plant babies – seeds

After pollination is achieved, and the flowers are fertilised, energy goes to seed production – job done, the flowers can slowly fade away. Seeds are extraordinary beings in their own right. Often a seed can live much longer than its parents – it is in this form that many plants spend most of their lives. They are time capsules that take the potential of a new plant into the future, whenever it is needed, wherever it is needed.

How do seeds protect themselves?

To survive its long wait or long journey the seed needs protection and seeds usually have coats and food reserves. Seed coats prevent moisture loss to prevent the young embryo inside from being eaten or drying out.

Some seeds are nestled in more complex protective structures – conifer seeds lie hidden in tough cones to reduce predation, for example. The seeds developing in the heart of the cones are nutritious and popular with birds, but often only those with the right beak structure can access them. Finches, Siskins and Crossbills are all well adapted for cone feeding.

These protective structures can be both a shield and a prison that the young plants must first escape from before they can grow. In many ways the coat controls the seed's development, just as our own defences can limit us sometimes. Gradually, over time and due to the effects of moisture, temperature changes and abrasion, the seed coat weakens, chemicals break down and the seedling can emerge.

Sometimes, as gardeners, we want to speed up the process of a young plant being able to emerge, and we can do this in several ways. One is by a process called scarification. This means simply chipping off or filing away part of the coat to let water and air in, as we do with sweet peas. Doing this mimics the effect of natural weathering over months or years. Another way is to soak seeds to soften the hard coat before sowing.

Time to leave home

The next challenge the seed faces is not when to grow, but where to grow. Seeds can rarely succeed in the shade of their parents or too many other plants – either because there is not enough light for all of them, too much competition for water and nutrients, or because of the pests and predators already gathered there, waiting for a young tender lunch. To survive, therefore, the seeds must get away to where there is less risk, more opportunity – they travel either in space or in time to find that ideal spot.

Because they have such an extraordinary ability to hibernate and lie dormant underground; one successful strategy for them is to wait until the coast is clear. Most seeds do this by entering deep dormancy until they get brought to the surface and they sense that a gap has formed in competing vegetation. They use light or temperature changes to know when they are at the surface again.

Seeds prefer freshly cleared soil to germinate in – recently turned or 'dug' soil tends to have more oxygen, and this also stimulates beneficial bacteria that support the seed or digest organic matter and provide a flush of nutrients, all helpful to get the baby plant established. The finer the soil structure, the better the contact between soil and seed and the easier it is for water and nutrients to pass between them.

In natural circumstances, landslips, storms that fell trees or wildfires all clear existing vegetation and disturb the soil, giving seeds the bed they need and the signal that opportunity is here – *carpe diem!*

At a smaller scale many animals also turn the soil, creating germination opportunities; birds, worms, moles, badgers and wild pigs may all do this. In our gardens, when we dig to create a 'seed bed', we are therefore mimicking a natural process that helps germination. Unfortunately, by doing so, we not only release the desired plants we have sown from hibernation but also many of those secreted away by nature beforehand. The thousands of seeds waiting in the soil are known as the seed bank.

Depending on their temperaments, and ours, we may see these spontaneous arrivals as welcome wildflowers, or even as 'weeds'. These seeds can wait patiently for months, years and decades for the right moment to start the cycle again. That moment may be a very long time coming. Recently scientists have successfully revived 32,000 year-old seeds, recovered from permafrost. Given such a long survival capability it is not uncommon for seeds to long outlive their parents. They can see human civilisations, presidents and many mistakes, come and go.

Seeds and spores are part of nature's backup plan. They live in refuges – deep underground or way above our heads – safe from earthly traumas and just waiting for their time to help with world weaving.

Seeds' travel plans

Like plants do generally, seeds follow different strategies to get to somewhere safe. Some are unambitious and just drop, keeping near to home. Here they must contend with shade from their parents and maybe pests and predators already established, so only the toughest and strongest dare to take this approach. They must be large heavy seed with lots of food reserves to give them a strong start, meaning that they could not go far anyway.

In contrast, some are adventurous and know they must leave home to thrive. The very tiniest, dust like seed may fly huge distances. They rely on travelling in thousands, wherever the wind takes them, so that at least a few will land where a perfect gap is waiting. Heavier seeds improve their flying ability by growing parachutes – like Dandelions – or at least a fluffy coat that catches the wind – Willow and Poplars do this. Others, like Sycamore or Ash, grow blades and twirl like helicopters.

The disadvantage of a flying strategy is that they inevitably have a baggage limit. So few flying seeds are really large, which means when they get to a new home they have few food reserves and cannot grow fast and big enough to compete with existing vegetation. This means that small-seeded plants rely on open habitats and fine soils where they have the best chance to germinate.

The very tiniest, more primitive plants – ferns and mosses, produce minute spores that mostly live in the air, floating free for weeks, months or even maybe years before they gradually drift to a suitable spot. They form part of the unseen floating ecosystem – the aeroplankton that surrounds us invisibly every day. These spores are able to make use of places that bigger seeds cannot get to – cliffs, roofs, tiny cracks in walls, gaps in pavements, etc.

Sometimes large seeds may need to travel too and to do this some have evolved their own unique techniques. Some, like coconuts or 'sea beans', take to the seas or rivers. It is likely that most of the plants you see colonising riverbanks or coasts, have seeds that float. Most large seeds rely on animal helpers to travel. To do this, some hitch a ride, they grow hooks and cling to the fur or clothes of passing animals (including people).

Fruity helpers
Fruits, seeds and animals are another of the great partnerships that the world depends on. For many seeds, the most reliable way to travel is to lure helpers with rewards of fruit. Most typically, seeds travel inside the gut of animals, including us. To get our services they grow delicious fruits around the seeds – brightly coloured or gently fragrant, so we don't miss them or resist them. As transport technology developed, these fruits travelled longer distances, eventually between continents – Tomatoes, for example, have been able to move tens of thousands of miles from their original home, and have become staples of regional cuisines, all thanks to their ability to attract mammals – especially humans.

The Apple is another example – it is believed to have originated as wild fruits in the mountains of Eurasia, specifically Kazakhstan. The fruit travelled with traders along the silk road, establishing in Europe where hybridisation and breeding lead to the diversity of apples that we know today, eventually complemented by varieties from Japan or USA, arriving on freight ships. One day, maybe, these seeds will travel with us to distant planets.

Plant shoots in waiting – the buds

As autumn approaches, the same time that the fruits are off travelling and the plant disassembling its leaves, flowers and other parts, the plant will also be forming the foundations for next year's regrowth; food is stored and buds are formed. Buds are protected by modified unexpanded leaves that are called bud scales. Inside these protective covers, a bud contains ready-made leaves and flowers, folded tight like a parachute. Just waiting their moment to be unfurled quickly when the plant needs them.

To get a quick start, buds also hold food stores, so sometimes they are food for us too (Brussels sprouts and capers for example) and for birds (Bullfinches are notorious for eating fruit tree buds).

Frondescence is the term for the unfolding of leaves from buds. In May or June it can happen so fast you can almost hear it. With new leaves and flowers in place, the plant is ready for its next growth cycle. It is time for roots to wake as well.

The hidden dimension – the roots

The visible, above-ground stems and leaves of plants are only part of the story; like an iceberg or an election there may be more beneath the surface than visible above. The part of the tree we can see is the above ground organ of a much bigger subterranean organism – roots that extend for tens of metres down and in every direction. The roots are host to a vast web of fungal hyphae that colonise the soil, as the leaves colonise the air. One day in a period of research for developing Eden Project, I found a tiny Willow seedling growing in the clay spoil heaps of mid Cornwall. The sapling was only 20cm tall but it had a root that ran for 4 metres through the spoil.

Tree roots usually radiate horizontally from the base of the

70

trunk, often near the surface, branching constantly to form a disc-like structure that is referred to as a root plate. The soil texture, soil structure and especially air availability determine the depth the roots grow in. On compacted land, like spoil heaps or under tarmac, roots will stay close to the surface looking for air, in doing so they may raise pavements and drive people crazy, especially local councils.

The availability of water and nutrients determine how much a root branches and proliferates; every day new fine roots are formed, absorb from the soil and die again, so there is a constant interchange – water and dissolved nutrients leave the soil organic matter and carbon returns. Roots track water and nutrients by following a gradient of moisture availability, when they find a rich spot, they increase their finest branches to create a greater surface area for absorption.

So plant roots are not just passive receivers of what flows to them, they actively forage and explore their patch and hunt out soil reserves. Some scientists even believe that roots can grow towards the sound of flowing water. Heading vertically down from a root plate may be several 'sinker roots' that are vital for accessing deep water reserves. As children we learn to draw trees with most of their roots heading down, but in reality most of the roots will grow near the surface. This is important to remember when doing any excavations near trees.

Roots have helpers too – the rhizosphere

One of the greatest revolutions of biological understanding this century is that there is no such thing as isolated individuals – every being on the Earth, including you, is a colony, an ecosystem of cooperation. Closely associated with the root system is a complex community of beings surrounding the roots like an underground cloud of life. This is called the rhizosphere.

Colonies of fungi and bacteria are fed by the roots, and in return they protect the plant from diseases and also harvest mineral nutrients for the plant to use. Some have specialised functions such as nitrogen fixing bacteria.

The rhizosphere is also there for information transfer. Latest research shows that some rhizosphere fungi can transfer food and information from one plant to another through the underground network – a mother plant can support her offspring until they are self-sufficient. A plant under attack from pests may use these connections to warn others to get their defences ready.

Roots are also the focus and regulators of many of the plant's key partnerships. Like the aboveground parts, they are summoners – they can summon beneficial partners and defenders by sending chemical messages and offering food rewards. The roots summon and sustain the rhizosphere organisms by feeding the soil around their roots, they release surplus food to help their partners grow. Most of the micro organisms that thrive in the rhizosphere are beneficial for plant growth, by defending plants from attack or by improving their ability to access resources and resist stresses.

The most important partnership for the plant is probably with a group of fungi called mycorrhizae. This partnership improves the capacity of the roots to gather water and nutrients; it is believed that these relationships are very ancient, they possibly first formed before plants had evolved roots of their own. Even today some plants, such as orchids, cannot survive on their own roots alone and must have fungal help. In fact, an orchid seed is so tiny it has almost no food reserves; the plant cannot even germinate without a fungal partner there to feed it.

And there is another crucial partnership that makes much of life on earth possible. This is between roots and a group of

Bodelva Pit before Eden Project.

Eden Project today.

Trees summon the rain they depend on.

Flowers give gifts to pollinators.

Flowers guide
the pollinators
to their nectar.

Leaves breathe
through pores.

Come and eat
my seeds.

After frondescence the leaf eaters get fresh salad at last.

Ivy flower.

Ivy in winter.

Ginkgo leaves.

Anthocyanin gives the red leaf colour.

Anthocyanins become more visible as chlorophyll fades.

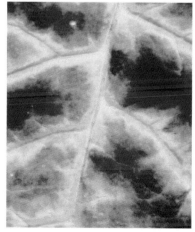

Flowers must provide safe and stable landing spots.

Fallen leaves do much good.

Puddles are mirrors and portals.

Ferns have spores not seeds.

Lichens on a garden bench.

Seeds preparing for flight.

Tree
returning
to air.

Dew spangled
web.

Bonfire
moss.

bacteria called nitrogen fixers. Beyond carbohydrates, made from carbon and water, nitrogen is the main element that plants need for growth, but there is a problem to be solved first. Nitrogen does not normally exist in the air or soil in a form they can use.

Nitrogen is essential for forming proteins and nucleic acids that cannot be made by simple photosynthesis. Although nitrogen is the most abundant gas in our atmosphere, it is an unreactive gas that needs to undergo a transformation into a soluble form before it is available to plant roots. This process is known as nitrogen fixation – this converts unreactive nitrogen gas into nitrates or ammonia, both of which can combine with other minerals to make soluble compounds that plants can use. There are two main ways that this can happen naturally. One is when lightning makes nitrogen react with oxygen to form soluble nitrates – a process we mimic in fertiliser factories.

Nitrogen fixation is carried out naturally in soil by certain bacteria. Some of these nitrogen-fixing bacteria have very close relationships with the roots of a few plant groups, especially legumes. The legumes, the pea and bean family of plants, form nodules on their roots to shelter these special bacteria. The plants supply them with food and get nitrogen compounds in return.

Then begins a magic that we all depend on. Clover too is from the legume family. Often in a lawn you will see that the patches where clover grows are much deeper green, fed by more nitrogen than the surrounding soil can supply. Lupins are also legumes – the name we give derives from the latin root Lupus' for wolf. In a confusion of cause and effect it was thought by the Romans that Lupin plants would eat fertility from soil, whereas, in fact, they were among the few plants that could survive in eroded infertile land, thanks to their bacteria partners, of course.

It is not only legumes that can develop such associations.

d

Related micro organisms can be found in nodules with tree and shrubs of different families. The most widespread tree species that do this include *Elaeagnus* (commonly used as a garden ornamental evergreen), *Alnus* (Alder) and *Casuarina*. The latter two are widely planted to stabilise and reclaim deserts or degraded lands that are deficient in nitrogen. If you visit the mining sites around Eden Project, along with Willow seedlings you will find many Alders growing on spoil heaps. As these species grow, slowly a more fertile soil builds in even the most hostile situations.

As the bacteria and plant materials die, the decomposers in the soil recycle the nitrogen for every other living thing to use. This relationship is also seen on rice roots, with the bacteria fixing nitrogen in rice paddies. Bacteria therefore provide the key nutrients to a global staple crop, and have done so long before fertilisers were invented.

Organic gardeners and farmers have long understood the importance of legumes in a crop rotation. Unlike most crops, growing legumes in a rotation can leave the soil more fertile rather than less. For a similar reason, beans are often seen as sacred food in traditional growing, they form a vital part of the three sisters growing system that indigenous Americans depended on through corn, bean and squash companion planting.

Death is not an ending

Through their lives plants give us many gifts, and even in death they continue to do so. Plants, especially trees, can be some of the oldest living organisms on Earth. Because of their modular forms and because they die in parts, rarely as a whole, and because they can regenerate from meristems, old age alone rarely ends a tree completely – disease, lightning, human attack, fires, storms or accidents are more often the causes of tree death.

Inevitably, there comes an end, of sorts. Even then, trees have more of an afterlife than most things. Life for trees continues after death in two main ways: Firstly, tree roots or stump meristems generate new shoots or even entire new trees from the existing root system. Some tree species actually rely on this as their main form of reproduction, using seed only to colonise distant places. An important group that does this is the Elm tree, regenerating from new young stems is the way they survive attacks from Elm diseases.

The possibilities that this regenerative ability presents are shown by Pando, a clone of the Quaking Aspen (*Populus tremuloides*). Pando lives in the Fishlake National Forest at the western edge of the Colorado Plateau in south-central Utah. This single tree occupies 43 hectares (106 acres) and is made up of roughly 47,000 connected trunks estimated to weigh collectively 6,000,000 kilograms, making it the heaviest known organism alive today. It was shown to be a single tree by genetic testing and it is believed to have one massive underground root system. The root system of Pando, at an estimated 80,000 years old, makes it therefore the oldest living plant on the Earth. This giant forest and this giant being grew from a tiny flying single seed and colonised its territory, thanks to meristems.

The second way that old trees live on is as a home for other creatures. After death, a decaying stump is soon alive again as a home for fungi, bacteria, and insects – the recycling squads. Slowly the body of the tree is released back into the air and the earth where it came from, but in their fading years they are very busy places. As the surfaces of the stump degrade and release nutrients, they become perfect homes for mosses and lichens too.

Very old decaying wood and trees are such rich habitats that sooner or later they carry more live biomass and cells than they did when they were alive. Keeping dead wood in your garden is therefore one of the best things that you can do for your neighbouring nature.

Plants, the world makers

Out of air, water, soil and light, plants weave a solid world of wonders – colours, scents, sounds and everything we need. They are world makers and wonder makers.

Be thankful for the plants for their world making, and for the gardens where we can meet them in their full splendour.

Chapter 2

The Tiny Things of the Garden

Now I would like to explore the very minute world of micro-organisms – the ones so tiny that we can't see them unaided. Alongside plants, it is these very minute things that do the most to keep the world vibrant and healthy. The lesson is that size isn't everything and key workers are easily overlooked.

Many of the tiny things living nearby are amongst the oldest known organisms – they have been around since the very origins of life and much of the world we see was made by them over millions of years. They haven't stopped, and with the plants they continue to be the world-makers.

Let us start our safari with the tiniest plants – the ones that live in pavement cracks and in the shadows of bark crevices but are no less amazing for that.

Mosses – the tiniest and most fragile

Mosses are amongst the most fragile of beings on land, many of their tissues are only one cell thick – they are life at its most diaphanous and delicate. Even so, and contrary to common belief, mosses do not only live in wet conditions. Despite their tissue-like substance, many are tough enough to survive quite dry places – on walls or roofs – as long as they are regularly refreshed with water. They can live there but they cannot reproduce without water.

In fact, if you have an old bonfire spot in your garden, look for a clump of moss that is a rich forest green, lined with silver and with auburn highlights. This is Bonfire moss, an oasis of beauty somehow thriving on a desert of dry ash. Bonfire moss could be the first moss you learn to name?

Mosses are selective about their growing conditions and different amounts of moisture, soil type and shade will suit different species. Different mosses will map out these variations in your garden, creating a mosaic of greens and textures.

Mosses are not as dependent on soil as most plants. They do not have roots, they have rudimentary root-like structures called rhizoids, but these are only for holding on. The plant absorbs all that it needs from air and rainfall. Because of this and because they are so tiny, mosses do not need vascular systems; they are in this regard like many aquatic plants.

Mossy fractals

Mosses grow in patterns and shapes that are classic fractal forms. If you look at them through a hand lens or magnifying glass, you will see complex shapes in infinite variety – spirals, caves, cloud-like forms and fairy castles. These are fractal forms.

Fractal is the name given to intricate shapes that repeat at different scales. Benoit Mandelbrot first coined the term 'fractal' in 1975, discovering that simple mathematic rules apply to a vast array of things that look visually chaotic. As he proved, fractal patterns are often found in nature's rough and complex patterns – in clouds, coastlines, plant leaves, ocean waves, in sounds sometimes, and even in rhythms of movement, like the shimmering of poplar leaves, the rise and fall of rivers, and in the clustering of galaxies.

Physicist and artist Richard Taylor found, through brainwave measurements, that when we contemplate fractal patterns in nature our brains enter a relaxed state, akin to meditation, or listening to music, resulting in reduced stress. Fractals absorb us, relax us, and help us reflect. Taylor believed that our brains are hardwired to relate to fractals in this way. Contemplating moss therefore is a boost for our mental health – moss gardens may be the ideal healing gardens.

Mosses as part of the web of life

Despite being so small, mosses are important in the garden ecosystem. They give shelter to many creatures, such as insects, who feed amongst them and lay eggs. In turn, this insect abundance provides much needed food for birds – that is why you often see birds sifting through moss in the garden.

Perfectionists sometimes see moss in lawns as a 'problem'. Remarkably there are even chemicals available to poison it. There seems to me to be a problem with this dominant gardening narrative. Perfection outranks abundance and diversity. Tidiness outranks curiosity.

Perfection and tidiness are not things our future depends on, but abundance and diversity are.

Because we fail to see the wonder in things, we judge them as outside our concept of perfection and we start killing, thereby blowing another hole in the web of life that sustains us. What madness has infected the human psyche that we feel an urge to poison something as fragile, as magical and as harmless and healing as moss?

We need more wabi-sabi.

The magical world of epiphytes

Lacking roots, mosses belong to a group of plants known as epiphytes, sometimes called air plants. Epiphytes can live above the soil, absorbing all of the water and nutrients they need from rainfall. In ancient times this was regarded as a supernatural ability and many epiphytes were honoured as magical beings. Many epiphytes are found on the branches and trunks of trees, getting additional sustenance from organic debris accumulating in fissures of the bark. These canopy dwellers are not parasites, they do no harm to the tree they live on.

Epiphytes are especially common in tropical rainforests. Many of the air plants that grow on trees there, such as orchids and bromeliads, are also homes to animals like Tree frogs. They make good houseplants too, which is how you may know them. In our colder climate we also have wild epiphytes, usually mosses, lichens and ferns. Orchids are not tree dwellers in the UK.

The temperate rainforest

Together, the lichens, mosses and fungi on old trees can create a spectacular and complex ecosystem. For these to approach their full abundance they need very humid air that is free from pollution. Where these conditions are found, especially in wet ancient woodland with many old, decaying trees, conditions are perfect for epiphytes and a remarkable mix can develop, creating rich communities known as temperate rainforest. These can be among the most biodiverse habitats on Earth. All they lack is large, wild animals, but who knows, there may be the odd black beast or two.

Temperate rainforests tend to prefer humid valleys on the west Atlantic coast but they can be found in other wet places. Wistman's Wood on Dartmoor is a renowned example of a temperate rainforest – it looks like a Tolkien dream with gnarled, twisted trees clinging on to huge moss-covered boulders.

You will not have such rich epiphyte communities in your garden. However, as long as the air quality is good, some epiphytes will be there somewhere, probably surviving on trees, walls, roofs, gutters and any other place where debris and moisture are held.

Old stone walls are like old dead trees. Gradually they gather more living cells than their original mass. Over time they become complex ecosystems and important habitats for many species. In our climate they are unlikely to support creatures as big as frogs, but every one of these will support a mini-ecosystem of tiny bugs and fungi and other creatures that feed on those bugs. One of the most remarkable will be the Moss Piglets.

Moss Piglets

A contender for the most extraordinary inhabitant of these tiny forests above the earth will be Tardigrades, also known as Moss Piglets or water bears. Tardigrades are microscopic animals, about 1mm in size. They like moist conditions but are very adaptable, they are even common in nylon carpets indoors. Tardigrades have a remarkable survival ability. They can enter a form of super hibernation known as a tun. In this state they can survive extreme stresses like boiling water or extreme cold. It has even been found that they can survive in space.

Bizarrely, an experiment testing this is already underway. In April 2019, an Israeli moon lander called Beresheet crashed on the moon, dumping its cargo amongst which were thousands of hibernating Tardigrades. As far as I know this was the first deliberate colonisation of the moon by an earthling! Although there is a chance that past asteroid impacts sent micro-organisms into space along with earth debris – some scientists speculate that moon colonists were already there. Can Tardigrades really survive on the moon? We don't know yet, but without doubt these extraordinary creatures, and the epiphytes, will be on earth for a very long time.

The wall dwellers

The nooks and crannies of walls are home to a surprising diversity of plants that probably first evolved to live on cliffs or exposed rock faces. Some, like the Ivy-leaved Toadflax (*Cymbalaria muralis*), have special adaptations for their rock-climbing lifestyle. This plant summons ants to help its seeds find the best germination spot. To do this the seeds provide a gift, a food parcel for the ants who carry it away and deposit it in a humid crevice. Other early wall-colonists like mosses, ferns and lichens travel there by airborne spores.

As organic debris accumulates in the crevices, enough soil-like materials are formed to allow establishment of larger wall loving plants. These typically include Red Valerian (*Centranthus ruber*), Mexican Fleabane or Spanish Daisy (*Erigeron mucronatus*) and as the name suggests, wall-flower (*Erysimum cheiri*).

Other plants that like dry stones are:

Stonecrop (*Sedum acre*), also known as Biting Stonecrop or Wall Pepper, can be found on walls or roof tiles growing as a mat. It is a succulent perennial with small, ovoid, fleshy leaves close to the stems. Flowers are yellow and star shaped, blooming from May to July, and bees love them.

Houseleeks (*Sempervivum*) are hardy succulent perennials forming mats of fleshy-leaved rosettes. They are often richly coloured, with star-shaped pink or pale yellow flowers in summer. Common Houseleek (*Sempervivum tectorium*) is also known as St Patrick's Cabbage. It is vigorous and forms mats of blue-green fleshy rosettes, tinged with reddish-purple. Houseleeks are edible but are described as 'diuretic' and 'purgative' so don't eat them before a journey or an important meeting!

Ivy (*Hedera helix*) is a familiar and common climber of walls, grabbing hold by adhesive suckers. Once in place it provides essential support for birds and insects with late flowers and berries and the winter shelter it provides. It is one of our few common native evergreens.

The Butterfly Bush (*Buddleia davidii*) originates from screes and cliff debris in the Himalayas and further east. After introduction to the UK, it quickly colonised derelict buildings and bomb sites, becoming widespread thanks to wartime destruction. It spreads easily with dust-like seeds that fly long distances and are well adapted for finding gaps in walls. Buddleia is sometimes disparaged for its non-native status and invasive nature, butterflies, however, care nothing for our opinions or labels and flock to this bush like no other.

Epiphytic ferns

We usually associate ferns with dark shady places but they often can grow in full sunlight and sometimes on trees, walls and roofs as well. Because of their microscopic airborne spores, they can land and germinate almost anywhere and therefore grow in many out of the way places.

A wide range of species that naturally occur on rocky habitats can be found in our gardens, preferring to have their roots in damp and sheltered crevices. These are some of the most common:

Hart's-tongue, *Asplenium scolopendrium* – this is probably the commonest wall species. The distinctive glossy strap-like fronds are unique amongst British ferns and make it easy to identify.

Rustyback, *Asplenium ceterach* – this small fern has wavy fronds. It has a brownish-red tint with a very scaly under-surface that makes it easy to recognise.

Wall-rue, *Asplenium ruta-muraria* – this is a very small delicate plant reminiscent of the houseplant the Maidenhair fern.

Black Spleenwort, *Asplenium adiantum-nigrum* – this has glossy, leathery leaves and distinctive blackish-brown stalks that are a bit swollen at its base.

Western Polypody, *Polypodium interjectum* – there are 3 native species of *Polypodium* fern in the UK, but this is by far the commonest in towns and gardens. They have thick, scaly, creeping roots (which are technically rhizomes or swollen stems) from which the fronds arise.

Now let us leave the tiny plants, and delve into another kingdom of life, the wondrous world of fungi.

Fungi – the world's super connectors

Despite what is sometimes thought, fungi are not strange zombie plants, they are an entirely different kingdom of life, unique and very different to both plants and animals. But if pushed to make a call, we would say they are closer to animals than plants. Fungi are not able to photosynthesise, so like animals they get their nutrition by digesting other creatures. The flesh of fungi is also closer to animal protein than it is to plant matter, hence mushrooms are valuable in a no-meat diet.

However, unlike animals, fungi excrete digestive enzymes that break down their food external to their bodies. To do this they form extensive fibrous webs, called mycelium. These webs colonise and consume every organic part of soil or dead organic matter, including dropped ice cream cones or dead creatures, all of your ancestors, back to the first ones that crawled from the sea. Even, sometimes, the heartwood of standing trees.

Fungi are therefore the great recyclers of the earth, they breakdown the dead and return the valuable raw materials for re-use. Without them the living would be buried by the dead. This is not a metaphor but a reality. Without fungi, the corpses of history would pile metres high, all nutrients locked up unavailable, and no new life able to emerge.

The most visible part of fungi, the mushrooms and toadstools, are the fungi equivalent of fruits, producing spores for the next generation. The mushrooms are a small part of the overall fungal body and are short lived. Yet they are the part we like to harvest and eat, so they become our focus for identification.

A secret network beneath our feet

We are only beginning to understand how vital fungal mycelium is for our world. Underneath our feet, in our gardens and everywhere we go, this vast complex web of fine filaments is working to clear dead things away and recycle nutrients. It is also providing a communication system. It is nature's internet. The web connects fungi together and connects plant roots too, in fact it connects all creatures of the rhizosphere.

Attached to the plants, this web extends their root systems, adding a vital extra capacity for gathering water and nutrients. This web also provides a channel for messages to pass between the plants, they warn each other of danger this way. This web is so extensive, there may be more biomass of a tree below ground than above. The tree we see, like a mushroom, is just the visible part, the fruiting body of a much larger subterranean organism.

Fungi can grow so big that one single specimen is another contender for the largest organism on Earth. This is a single honey fungus measuring 2.4 miles (3.8 km) across. It has not revealed its name yet so let's call it 'Honey'. Honey lives in the Blue Mountains in Oregon and is thought to be somewhere between 1,900 and 8,650 years old.

Maybe your whole town or village is also connected by one

underground web, with every garden sending messages to the others?

Micro-organisms are very ancient and are still world-making. They are still evolving new capabilities too. Evidence of this comes clearly from Radiotrophic fungi. Radiotrophic fungi have recently evolved the ability to radiosynthesise, that is, they use a pigment to make food like plants do. In this case it is a dark pigment called melanin that we also have in our hair and skin. The Radiotrophic fungi use this pigment to capture gamma radiation and convert it into chemical energy for growth. This echoes how plants use the pigment chlorophyll to capture and convert light radiation. These fungi are found growing in and around the nuclear reactor of Chernobyl. This is an important confirmation that life finds ways to thrive in unlikely places; whatever we throw at it, life finds a way.

Given the vast significance of photosynthesis to all biodiversity, including humans, who knows what wonders may follow now that fungi have invented an alternative. One emerging use is already apparent. Space researchers have looked at the ability of these fungi to survive in space under high radiation levels and they are being considered for use as radiation shields. Scientists also speculate that these fungi could be used to provide building materials, recycling systems and maybe food for Mars colonisation. Fungi, worms, plants and Tardigrades – that Mars mission is starting to look as crowded as Noah's voyage, which is a reminder of what sustains us here on Earth – the plants and the tiny things mostly.

Lichens – nature's most patient tiny things

There can be few living things that look as insignificant as lichens, they can seem just like crusty smudges of pale green, grey or bilious yellow. This camouflage is deceptive as lichens are some of the most powerful and unique creatures we see in nature. They are formed from a symbiosis (mutually supportive partnership) of up to two fungi and an algae – the algae photosynthesises and feeds the fungi, the fungi provides shelter and gathers nutrients.

Lichens ask so little from the world, they can grow almost anywhere that is not polluted. Most lichens hug close to their home plant, or stone, some, however, can develop more complex structures, resembling mosses. If the air is clear in your garden you will find them on any stable undisturbed surface – walls, rocks, or benches maybe. They can grow on trees, if not too shaded or fast growing. In the lifetime of a lichen, the stretching of bark on a fast-growing tree would be like an earthquake.

To get the few nutrients they need, the lichens secrete powerful acids that release the nutrients from the minerals they are perched on. Over time, and lichens have lots of time, these acids, combined with the weather, can reduce boulders, rocks, mountains, abandoned factories and, one day, even skyscrapers to dust. Giant structures are turned to small particles that later join with dead organic matter to form the soil that all life depends on.

Lichens bring inorganic matter into the living world. They are also key workers therefore. Without their persistent work over millions of years we would starve. They don't get the press that pollinators do, their work is more subtle. We need them nevertheless.

Slime moulds – bizarre kingdom of their own

If you are really observant, you may add yet another entire kingdom of life to your garden spotting; a slime mould. Slime moulds are not plants, animals or fungi (most moulds are fungi), they are part of a kingdom known as protists. Protists have been described by scientists as a group 'we put things in that we don't understand'. Surely this is a long, long list by now. Naming no names, are protists eligible to run for election?

The most likely place to find slime moulds is on rotting wood in the summer, looking either like a yellow smear or like a blob. They will never be chosen for postcard shots. In some ways the slime moulds give us a glimpse of prehistory. They are single-celled creatures that form colonies to do more ambitious things – just like we believe the first complex creatures did millions of years ago.

Despite being built like an ancient throwback, they have amazed scientists by showing apparent problem-solving ability. A slime mould colony placed in a maze can solve the puzzle to find the shortest route to food. They eat micro-organisms that are digesting dead plants. For a while, a problem-solving slime mould became an attraction at the Paris zoo.

Yeasts – the party makers and the future makers

Yeasts are single celled, non filamentous fungi – they don't form webs and are too small to see by eye, we just see their workings. These free-living, single-celled fungi are everywhere, in the air and on every surface. They get their nutrition by fermenting – we use them to make bread and every form of alcohol. Without yeasts, no sandwiches, no pizzas, no beer.

The first yeasts used for fermenting our foods were ones that drifted naturally onto food material. They arrived naturally, in fact we couldn't stop them. This traditional technique is just how many have made sourdough bread during the Covid-19 lockdown. Observing the actions of wild yeasts is believed to be how people first learnt to brew beer, which happened soon after cereal growing became widespread. Evidence of brewing beer dates from 10,000 BC in Mesopotamia. Wild yeasts are also found on wine skins, so the first wines were probably developed in the same way.

Working with yeasts to process foods is regarded as the first human venture into biotechnology. Most of our successes to date have come from partnership with one yeast species *Saccharomyces cerevisiae* and its close relatives. Today we know of 1500 other yeast species and there are probably many more, sometimes referred to as 'non-conventional yeasts'. These can feed on many different materials.

Researchers see enormous potential for biotechnological advances, as working with these less studied yeasts may help us produce new foods, new materials and new medicines. Almost certainly the yeasts will also join the space race.

Bacteria – the most maligned tiny thing

Bacteria are also microscopic single-celled organisms that, like fungi and slime moulds, are neither plants or animals. The oldest known fossils are of bacteria-like organisms. Bacteria and viruses are thought to have been the first life to appear on earth, about 4 billion years ago. They had the Earth to themselves for billions of years, before things got more interesting and other marvels arrived alongside to mix things up a bit. Bacteria are incredibly successful and well adapted. Today they exist in countless numbers everywhere we look, in almost every environment, both inside and outside other organisms.

A gram of soil typically contains about 40 million bacterial cells. A millilitre of fresh water usually holds about one million bacterial cells. The earth is estimated to hold at least 5 nonillion bacteria, and much of the earth's biomass is thought to be made of bacteria. (Unlike eleventy-one, a nonillion is a real number not something Trump invented – look it up.)

Bacteria can feed in many different ways, and only a few are harmful. Some bacteria, like fungi, get their energy through consuming dead material. Admittedly a few are diseases that attack and kill their host before they eat it. Yet many bacteria are helpful. We would not exist without them.

Like plants, some bacteria make their own food. They do this either through photosynthesis, using sunlight, water and carbon dioxide, or chemosynthesis, using carbon dioxide, water, and other chemicals such as ammonia, nitrogen and sulphur, combining them in ways that produce useful compounds and release energy. Photosynthesising bacteria, a group known as cyanobacteria, also produce oxygen. They invented photosynthesis before plants and taught the plants how to do it. These creatures probably were the first to release free oxygen into the earth's atmosphere before plants evolved to do the same.

Actually, the chloroplasts in plants that do the photosynthesis are believed to be descendants of cyanobacteria that moved inside and entered into close symbiosis with plants. The bacteria that use chemosynthesis are found in ocean vents and as nitrogen fixers in the roots of legumes and in rice paddies and wetlands.

Everywhere you can imagine

There are bacteria way above us in the stratosphere, between 6 and 30 miles up in the atmosphere, and in the ocean depths, down to 10,000 metres deep. The subsurface of the Earth holds about 90% of the biomass of bacteria, and 15% of the total biomass for all life.

The deep biosphere is the newly discovered community of living organisms that live well below the first few metres of the surface. This community extends down at least 5 kilometres below the continental surface and 10.5 kilometres below the surface of the seas. They also survive in volcanic vents at temperatures that may reach beyond 100°C.

Aside from these volcanoes, there is very little usable energy available at these great depths, so their metabolisms can be up to a million times slower than at the surface. These deep-living bacteria may live for thousands of years before dividing and there is no known limit to their age. Recently researchers have found and revived bacteria from deep sea trenches where they are thought to have survived for 100 million years. Far, far longer than humans have existed, these bacteria have been in lockdown.

Bacteria and human health

Many of the bacteria in our bodies play an important role in our survival. Bacteria in our digestive systems break down nutrients, such as complex sugars, into forms our bodies can use. Non-hazardous bacteria also prevent diseases by occupying places that disease-causing organisms want to attach to. Some bacteria also protect us from disease by attacking pathogens.

Recent research has shown in increasing detail how the human body interacts with bacteria, and particularly the huge populations of bacteria living in the intestinal tract, known as the gut microbiome. The bacteria in our microbiome help us to digest our food and they help to protect us against other bacteria that cause disease. They also produce vitamins, including the B vitamins – B12, thiamine and riboflavin – and vitamin K which is needed for blood coagulation.

Increasingly scientists understand that no organism operates truly independent of others – like trees and fungi we are all networked and communicating constantly with others that help us to survive. As Anna Tsing says: "There is no such thing as 'alone' in modern biological understanding."

The human superorganism

Collectively, the genetic material of the microbiome is approximately 150 times greater than the human genome, which has led some scientists to label our bodies and microbiome combined as a 'superorganism'. We meet other garden superorganisms later.

Within the human gut, there is on average 100 trillion bacteria of thousands of different types which is around 10 times more than there are cells in the human body – so no human is an individual, no more than a tree is. We are all walking ecosystems, multitudes of complex communicating and collaborating communities, of which the human cells are the minority. This means that in the unlikely event that you are probed by an alien and samples taken, they would conclude that you are a big bacteria and that bacteria are the most intelligent life on Earth. Maybe they are.

Our gut microbiome health affects how our immune system responds to unwanted microbes, like viruses, entering the body. Our immune system is better at fighting infections if the colony of gut microbes is diverse and healthy. Evidence is growing that gut bacteria also play a role in mitigating the development of food allergies. The gut microbiome has also been linked to asthma and autism, and the skin microbiome is responsible for acne. Recently the absence of a healthy diversity of gut bacteria has been linked to Alzheimer's. Healthier partnerships with the bacteria of our bodies could be the key to solving many ailments.

The links between gut and brain also mean that our brains can influence digestion and gut health. Healthy mind, healthy body.

Support the microbiome

Inspired by the superorganism insight and the obvious co-evolution of humans and microbes, research is intensifying.

We are on the verge of a revolution in approaches to health care. We can expect to see less emphasis on antibiotics and disinfectants and more use of probiotics, which are foods or chemicals that support these beneficial partnerships. Researchers are already clear that exposure to microbe-rich environments is important to our health. The more diverse the environments we are exposed to, the richer our personal microbiomes become. Everywhere we live, every other being we are in close contact with, introduces us to another group of organisms that may join our internal community. In particular, there is interest in how to ensure that children are exposed to the right conditions to build a healthy microbiome and develop protections against allergies.

New discoveries are coming constantly. Recently researchers have found several species of gut bacteria are missing in people with depression. Many gut bacteria make substances that affect nerve cell function – and even influence mood. For example, a common soil bacteria, *Mycobacterium vaccae*, seems to increase happiness and reduce depression. Breathing in the aroma of freshly dug soil really is good for you.

No doubt in years to come bacteria will reveal other ways they help us. In the meantime, we know for sure that messing around in the garden and getting messy is a good idea. Like the plants we are sustained by the soil and our partnerships within it.

Maybe in some sense we too are the above-ground fruits of a vast subterranean organism?

If you have a pond in your garden or nearby, you should regard the scum it forms with new respect. The scum is probably cyanobacteria, the first organisms to invent photosynthesis over 4 billion years ago. Without them, no green plants, no flowers, trees or even seaweeds, therefore no birds, no fish, no people.

Pause a moment and say thank you to the scum. Don't judge too quickly. Key workers can be overlooked easily.

Chapter 3

The Small Things

Here we move on from the micro to the small garden animals that also do so much for us.

Fairies in the garden

I would like to start with the smallest of the insects, the Fairy wasp of the Mymiridae family. They are so small you probably had no idea they existed, but like many small creatures they are helpers for us. The family that these fairies belong to includes the smallest known insects in the world. Most species are less than 1mm long. Not surprisingly, they are hard to spot and study. Even so, we know of 1,400 species. Many of them live in the tropics but some are found much closer to home.

Fairy wasps are minute, feathery-winged parasitic wasps. They are also called 'Fairy flies'. The Fairy wasp larvae are the parasites. Adult females search for the eggs of other insects in sheltered places, such as under leaves or in leaf litter. She lays her eggs inside the other eggs. The wasp larva uses the nutrients from the host egg to develop into an adult.

After emerging, adult Fairy wasps only live for a couple of days, during which they must reproduce and start the cycle again. Not only are they small but they are only here for brief moments, just as fairies are supposed to behave. Some males never see much more than the egg they develop in – as soon as they emerge from their own egg within an egg, they mate with a female and die.

When Jenny Owen undertook her landmark 30 year study of life in her Leicester garden, she found a remarkable abundance. Over 8000 species including one third of all known UK insects were living there. This abundance also included four species new to science, ones that had never been seen before, not anywhere else than her Leicester garden. These new species were Fairy wasps.

Fairy wasps are an example of how much biodiversity is still undiscovered, even on our doorsteps. We still have much to learn about the ecology and life history of the minuscule Fairy wasp.

Despite their diminutive size and hidden lives, we do know that the Fairy wasps are important in controlling populations of many other insects. Most of the known Fairy wasps parasitise Hemiptera species, the group of plant-sucking bugs that includes plant-hoppers and aphids. For this reason, some species are used as biological control agents in farming to control damaging pests.

Fortunately we can support the fairies without seeing them. Like many other flying insects, adults need sugar from floral nectar for their energy. Flowers, including 'weeds', support the fairies and many other beneficial insects, so grow lots of flowers if you can.

Pesticides will kill Fairy wasps, or make them less effective at controlling other pests. Even if you have many garden pests, leave the poisons in the garden centre. You probably have fairies in the garden that will help control the Greenfly for you.

And down came a spider

The Fairy wasps are not alone in the work of controlling problems for us. Spiders are probably the most important group of insect pest controllers that we have as allies. The small shiny black spider we call Money spider is another important helper. They are one of the smallest spiders at just 3mm in size, but they are still good hunters with a great fondness for aphids.

Money spiders belong to the huge family Linyphiidae that includes over 270 species of spider known so far. Like the Fairy flies, this family is still revealing new members. The Money spiders are found almost everywhere because they are good at getting about. Because of their small size they can use a method of dispersal called 'ballooning'. The spider lets out a strand of silk into the air, wind currents lift the simple thread and the spider flies with it. At certain times of the year many millions of spiders are drifting above you. This is why spiders occasionally get caught in people's hair – it was thought when this happened the person would be coming into money – hence the name Money spider.

Web masters

Many different kinds of spiders are likely to be hunting in your garden. The webs they make are carefully designed in their size, shape and position to catch their prey. Some spiders target flying insects and will position their webs on popular flight paths such as near night lights that moths are drawn to. These include the classic circular web, made by Orb spiders that we are all familiar with. Some spiders build horizontal webs to catch prey that fall from trees in windy weather. These are known as sheet webs and include those made by Money spiders.

Webs low down are designed to catch crawling insects such as those made by the Labyrinth spider that typically builds its traps under bushes, in tall grass and other dense vegetation. This is a similar technique to that used by the Funnel-web spider in Australia.

Tube web spiders do not use their web to catch their prey, but rather build a den to hide in, usually in cracks in walls. They then lay a series of trip wires as an alarm system. When dinner arrives, the spider gets a signal and pounces from its hiding spot. Other jumping spiders like the Wolf spider, Crab spider and Woodlouse spider, also do not rely on webs but lie in wait to ambush passing prey. Crab spiders frequently hide in flowers, camouflaged by colours and hues that match the flowers. If you see a crab-like white spider sitting on a flower it is likely to be one of these. It can be quite a shock to see what you thought was part of a flower, rise up, jump on a butterfly and start to eat it.

Garden spiders usually weave their webs through the night, leaving the dew-spangled wonders for us to find in the morning. Through the summer, webs often remain invisible to us, but in autumn and winter mist droplets or frost make them obvious and give the impression that crowds of spiders have suddenly arrived.

Spider thread is an amazing substance. One single web may contain up to 60 metres of thread yet weigh only 1 milligram. Because the web is so thin, it requires careful design to withstand the impact of blundering insects that fly into it. The web is designed to dissipate shocks and rebound rather than break on impact.

Spider webs do not just help in the garden, but potentially they may one day supply many of our other needs. Researchers are busy looking at whether we can learn from spider webs to create materials with many uses, from surgery aids to bullet-proof clothing, acoustic sensors and furniture. These are all being modelled on web design. If not the spiders, their designs may also join the space race.

Moths, the night pollinators

Another group of small garden workers we should not overlook are the moths. There are about 2,500 moth species found in

97

e

Britain and Ireland. Of these there are about 900 larger moths called macro-moths and these are the ones that blunder into the house, knock themselves stupid against lights or sit bewildered on the window. Most of our garden moths therefore are the smaller or micro-moths.

Micro-moths

Like their cousins the larger moths and butterflies, these tiny flyers are useful pollinators. As larvae, however, they can cause trouble. Leaf mining pests are micro-moths because their caterpillars burrow into leaves and eat them from the inside. Clothes moths and Carpet moths are micro-moth larvae too. Although we hate them for the damage they can do inside the house, in the garden these species have important jobs to do.

While the larvae of most micro-moths feed on plant material, a few are important recyclers of things others can't digest, such as hair, feathers and other animal remains. Without the work of these caterpillars, fleeces, fur and feathers would linger for years wherever an animal died. Animals often withdraw to their burrows or other secluded spots before they die, so the female moths are evolved to explore dark, confined spaces. To them a wardrobe containing your old jumpers looks like a den complete with animal pelt, and they start doing what they evolved to do, unaware that the clothes were still wanted (or were they? Surely time for a clear out by now!).

Other micro moths recycle other less digestible remains, ferns, fungi and old birds' nests. Micro-moths are known to be difficult to spot and identify, some however are distinctive and exquisitely beautiful. Easiest to identify is probably the White Plume moth (*Pterophorus pentadactyla*). The Plume moths possess intricately divided, often feather-like, wings. Like the majority of micro-moths, the White Plume moth is most active during the night when it feeds on flowers, but it may be seen during the day if its roost is disturbed. Because of its colour you may even spot it resting. The caterpillars of the White Plume moth feed on the dreaded Bindweed, the bane of many gardeners. Everything plays a part in the network of life. If your garden is being swallowed by Bindweed, encourage the moths to eat it.

The Common Grass-veneer is another micro-moth you may see. Like those of most grass moths, its caterpillars feed exclusively on grasses. This is one of the reasons why it is good to leave a tiny patch of uncut grass in your garden.

Meet another superorganism, the ants

We can't discuss the important members of the garden community without talking of the ants. Flowers and pollinators are not the only plant-insect partnerships of great importance, plants and ants have struck a different bargain.

Ants aren't just picnic irritants; they are useful and remarkable members of the garden community. Along with worms, ants are important for turning the soil, letting water soak in more easily and creating air channels for roots. Ants are also important for seed dispersal. 5% of all plants have their seeds dispersed by insects and it is usually ants that do this work.

Ants are also plant protectors. They patrol their patch keeping plant enemies away. They also secrete anti-microbial chemicals and it is believed these may also help protect their adopted plants from diseases. Because most ants don't eat plants directly, their work is rewarded another way. Some plants have evolved seed with packets of ant food attached as enticements. The ants will carry the seed away, often to a burrow where they have already gathered organic matter, providing a nutrient rich location for the seed to germinate.

Some trees and shrubs also produce what are known as

'extrafloral nectaries'. These are feeding stations on the stems that are available to ants without the hassle of a flower to navigate. Many tropical trees do this. Elderberry bushes are the most common garden plant where you will see this happening. The fact that plants have evolved to do this is evidence of how they need the ants.

Ants may feed on plants through an intermediary. Some ants have learnt how to farm aphids, scale insects, or other bugs that feed on plant sap. The ant gathers the excess sap (also known as honeydew) that the bugs can't manage. If you have a bush or tree with large colonies of aphids, look closely and you will probably see patrolling ants. If so, you are peering at a farm, a honeydew farm.

Great day for a flight wedding

In ant societies, the queen, workers and warriors are all female; the male is only there for reproduction. Once a year there can be a spectacular wedding ceremony, in preparation for which they get special outfits – the ants grow wings.

In summer, there comes a moment when the ground is crawling with these winged ants. Then they take to the skies. Ant wings are temporary and they are not powerful flyers. They require good weather conditions, with no wind or rain. The flying therefore usually occurs in July or August during a period of hot and humid weather (if we get one). Because weather is critical, winged ants appear at different times around the country and the precise timing of flying varies from year to year. The ants can sense when the moment is approaching, they are good at weather forecasting.

Prior to flying, the ants are going about their everyday business in a colony underground. In the few weeks before the flight, you may see heaps of soil appearing above the nests, this is a sign that things are getting busy in preparation down below.

Ants often fly earlier in urban areas because temperatures are warmer. The appearance of winged ants may extend over several weeks from different colonies, although there are peaks, each lasting only a few days. The temperature and humidity that triggers swarming and flight time is different for each species. Black garden ants are the ones you are most likely to see swarming. They like to nest in warm dry soil and you often find them in flower beds and lawns, and under paving slabs or stones.

The remarkable society of ants

Ants aren't just useful, they are also extraordinary creatures that design and live in complex societies. Let's consider a question that looks simple on the surface. How many ants are there in your garden? The answer may be more surprising than you imagine – your garden probably has around a thousand individual ants per square metre. However, ants have such complex and cooperative social lives that some scientists believe the idea of individuals has little meaning and this is not how we should see them. Each colony could be seen as one 'superorganism'. Just as the human body is really a superorganism made up of part human and larger part bacteria. So rather than many thousand individuals, you may have half a dozen ant super-creatures patrolling the garden and keeping your plants safe from harm.

Ants create complex caste systems where individuals specialise and have different roles. The queen's sole duty is to lay the eggs, while female workers look after the queen, eggs and larvae. The ants you see patrolling for most of the year are these female workers gathering food for the colony. The workers also build the nest and otherwise ensure the colony runs smoothly. The only duty for male ants is to mate with the queen, otherwise they do little.

Most of the eggs develop into workers, but when the colony

is ready, the queen begins to produce virgin queens and males. At some point a virgin queen must leave to begin a new colony. When the winged males (drones) and virgin queens emerge from the nest, they scatter to maximise the chance of mating between different colonies and to reduce inbreeding. The virgin queen flies, meets and mates with a male from a different colony and finds a new area in which to start building her new nest. The large-winged females and the smaller winged males are sometimes seen flying whilst mating. This is known as the nuptial flight.

After the ants have mated, the role of the males is over. The mated queens then chew off their own wings and search for a suitable site in which to make the new colony. This is why you often see large ants walking around after a 'flying ant day' looking dazed and you may see discarded wings scattered around. Once the newly mated queen has found a suitable site, she digs herself an underground chamber and lays her first few eggs, which she rears to adulthood. She won't eat for weeks, not until her first brood of daughter workers are ready to forage food for her.

The stock of sperm the queen received during the nuptial flight will serve for her to lay fertilised eggs for the rest of her lifetime. That may be fifteen years or more. She will continue to reproduce until a colony is thousands strong and large nests can have more than 20,000 workers. After the nuptial flight, the male ants usually only live for another day or two, so not much more than a week in total. These swarming events do not just benefit the ant colonies, they provide a food resource for many birds. Swifts often feed from flying swarms of ants.

The complexity and advanced cooperation of ant behaviour inspired the great conservation ecologist E.O. Wilson and launched a remarkable career. Based on his observations of ant ecology, Wilson pioneered many new fields including sociobiology and biophilia (the idea that evolution has left humans with a requirement for contact with other species and nature). Wilson undertook most of his research by observing ant societies in South American rainforests. Fortunately, we do not need to travel so far – the extraordinary societies of ants are everywhere, including just outside our windows. Who knows how many future conservation greats will be inspired too by observation of nearby nature?

So when it comes to the small things, just because it is hard to see what they do for us, be assured they do a lot. Their smallness does not mean that they aren't important. They too are key workers that keep our world functioning and filled with wonders.

Chapter 4

The Larger Animals
of the Garden

Alongside plants, fungi and bacteria, the larger invertebrates are the most numerous and probably the next most important group of organisms in your garden. So let's get to know them and the important things they do for us and the world around us.

The arthropods

Arthropods is the name given to a group of animals that encompasses insects, shellfish, spiders and mites. The arthropods is the largest group of all animals, both in species diversity and biomass.

Arthropods have a hard body coat known as an exoskeleton; to make this they need a protein called chitin and lots of it. This material is the same as fungi build their bodies from. Unlike carbohydrates that make up the majority of the wood and structure of most plants, proteins are chemicals that need nitrogen but, as we have seen, plants cannot weave a world with nitrogen until it is transformed from gas to a soluble form.

Arthropods and the rest of us could not exist at all before bacteria first invented the alchemical transformation of nitrogen into a usable form, or before plants converted that nitrogen into food. Because of their enormous combined biomass, the evolution of arthropods changed the balance of chemical demand to sustain life. Lots of nitrogen was needed to build bodies, more than ever before.

William Bryant Logan writes:

'If there were no death, no decomposers, the nitrogen would build up in the dirt, deserting the air. The exoskeleton of insects is made of nitrogen-containing chitin. If this material alone were not decayed and decomposed by fungi, bacteria and the sun, the atmosphere would have been bare of nitrogen within forty million years of the insect's arrival.'

So this helps us to understand the importance of the clean-up and recycling creatures, and also confirms the importance of nitrogen fixing bacteria. Without them, no arthropods, no proteins, no steaks, and no people to enjoy them.

With arthropods joining the cast, what do they bring to the garden?

The pollinators

Amongst the arthropods, pollinators get all of the good press at the moment. Other insects and their contribution to a healthy world tend to be overlooked, yet each plays its role in keeping our environment functioning as it should.

Pollinators are the essential partners that plants use for reproduction to carry the male 'sperm' (the pollen) to the female. For most of our garden plants and our crops, pollinating insects are essential for their, and our, survival.

Although the bees are probably the best known pollinators, there are many other different types – butterflies, moths, beetles, hoverflies, wasps and even ants. Let's meet some of them.

Bees – the most popular pollinators

In a 2020 meeting of the Royal Geographical Society of London, the Earthwatch Institute declared bees the most important living organisms on this planet, although I suspect the bacteria have a claim too. Because of this and probably because of their endearing appearance, we love the bees. So I want to take a quick tour of the diversity of bees you may find in your garden. You may learn of some you may have seen but not realised they are bees at all.

There are many kinds of bee (4000 species in the USA alone). There are more than 250 species of bee in the UK, including numblebees, mason bees, mining bees and bees specific to one plant type. All are important pollinators.

Plasterer bees

Plasterer bees are a widespread group of bees with short tongues which nest in underground burrows. They are known as plasterer bees because they use a resin to line their burrows. Common plasterers in the UK are the Ivy Mining bees (*Colletes hederae*). This bee is the largest member of the family and is a specialist of ivy flowers, emerging in September. Ivy bees are amongst the latest bees to still fly in our gardens before they retreat to their winter hibernation. The Ivy bee is a recent addition to the UK and is currently expanding northwards into northern England and Scotland.

Davies Mining bee (*Colletes daviesanus)* is a smaller plasterer bee that is active mid-summer and is seen often on flowers of the Compositae family of plants, such as the Lawn Daisy, Ox-eye Daisy and Yarrow (*Achillea*). Composite means that what we see as one large flower is in fact many smaller ones jammed together – the family includes anything that looks like a Daisy, including Sunflowers and Crysanthemums.

Related to the plasterer bees are *Hylaeus* bees, known as Yellow-faced bees because of their distinctive facial markings. *Hylaeus* bees also like composite flowers and can often be found on *Astrantia* and Sea Holly (*Eryngium*). One of the most widespread members of this genus is the Common Yellow-faced bee, *Hylaeus communis*.

Blood bees

The *Halictus* bees are also known as Furrow bees, Sweat bees or sometimes Blood bees, named because of their blood red colouration. All have short tongues and they again prefer simple open flowers. They are very small bees and are attracted to small flowers like *Astrantia*, Allium, Thyme, Sea Holly (*Eryngium*) and Golden Rod (*Solidago*).

The specialist bees

Melitta bees are a small and specialised family of bees with 4 species in the UK. They specialise on chalk grassland flowers. Usually they are countryside rather than urban bees, although the Clover bee *Melitta leporina* can sometimes be found on industrial wasteland where crushed concrete and rubble support the lime loving food plants they rely on.

The Gold-tailed bee *Melitta haemorrhoidalis* is a specialist of Bellflowers (*Campanula*) and can be found in gardens where it collects pollen from Canterbury Bells and other Bellflowers.

The *Macropis* bees have a single UK representative – this is the highly specialised Yellow Loosestrife bee *Macropis europaea*, which collects oils from Yellow Loosestrife flowers to line and waterproof its nest burrows as it frequently nests in damp soils. They collect pollen exclusively from the Yellow Loosestrife flowers which grow in damp ground around streams and pond margins.

The bumblebees

Bumblebees are probably the most familiar of all bees. There are 27 species in the UK which vary in size and colour. Many are black and yellow with coloured tails, some are mostly black and some are mostly brown. All are covered in dense fur.

Bumblebees are social, they nest in colonies ranging from a few dozen to several hundred workers with one queen. Eight species are common and widespread in the UK. Not all Bumblebees are as benign as they look. Some, such as the Southern Cuckoo bee, *Bombus vestalis*, are parasites of other bees.

The most common bumblebee species include The Early bumblebee *(Bombus pratorum);* it is one of the most widespread and abundant species. This is a small bee with a red tail. As the common name suggests, this is among the earliest bumblebees to emerge from hibernation each year and males can be seen flying as early as February. They are therefore reliant on the first flowers – spring bulbs and Willow catkins amongst them.

The Early bumblebee is usually smaller and more of a dull orange than the similar Red-tailed bumblebee *(Bombus lapidarius)*. Red-tailed bumblebees are one of the UK's most widespread bee species. The females are jet black with a bright red or orange tail, while males have a yellow head and collar and a yellow midriff band. These bees are found in a variety of habitats anywhere they can find the common flowers that they like, such as Thistles, Bird's Foot Trefoil and Buddleia.

Tree bumblebees *(Bombus hypnorum)* are one of our most common pollinator species. They are identified by their ginger thorax, black abdomen and white tail. They are found in habitats ranging from woodland to garden, and sometimes even nesting in old bird boxes. Some of their favourite flowers include Rhododendrons, Brambles and Comfrey.

Also common are White-tailed bumblebees, that have a bright yellow collar, yellow abdomen band and bright white tail. They can be found almost anywhere, feeding on a wide range of flowers, including Thistles, Buddleia, Brambles and Scabious.

Common Carder bees (*Bombus pascuorum*) are a type of bumblebee, found everywhere from arable land to urban gardens. These little bees are ginger or light brown all over with no white tail. Gorse is a favourite food plant, alongside Dandelions, Bluebells, Dead-nettles, Comfrey, Selfheal and Foxgloves. So leaving wild patches in your garden or nearby will especially help these bees.

The Flower bees

The Flower bees of the genus *Anthophora* are solitary bees. The most numerous and recognisable member of the group is the Hairy-footed Flower bee *Anthophora plumipes* which is another of our first bees to emerge in spring. They have exceptionally long tongues so can feed from larger flowers than the short-tongued bees. They like *Pulmonaria* and Snapdragon flowers. These bees often nest in old walls and chimneys where they excavate burrows in decaying mortar. This is something that Mason bees do too. Their cousins, the Green-eyed Flower bee *Anthophora bimaculata* and the Fork-tailed Flower bee *Anthophora furcata* are less common.

Parasitic bees

The Mourning bee *Melecta albifrons* is a parasite of the Hairy-footed Flower bee and can often be found close to their hosts' nest spots. It is easy to recognise with its black body and white spots. They sometimes follow the flower bees around, hoping to find out where their nests are.

The Nomada bees are wasp-like parasitic bees which lay their eggs into the nests of mining bees (*Andrena* species). They eat the hosts' eggs and offspring, and pollen cache. They are difficult bees to identify – they are less hairy than many bees and look more like wasps.

A growing diversity of bees

This amazing diversity of bees is being added to by new arrivals, like the Ivy bee. One of the most recent arrivals is the massive bright purple Violet Carpenter bee *Xylocopa violacea*. This is the UK's largest bee. Widespread and common on the continent, this bee needs a warm climate. It is expanding its range and with climate change may soon be seen more frequently in the UK, especially in cities.

Mason bees

If you have ever noticed clouds of bees hovering about in front of walls, and now and then diving into a cavity, they are likely to be mason bees; a group of solitary bees that nest in holes in trees, walls and hollow stems.

The mason bee you are most likely to see is the Red mason bee *Osmia bicornis*. These are also the bees most likely to be staying in your bee hotel. Look out for a black head, brown thorax and orange abdomen, and in females, a lot of fluff! Their food plants include Willow and fruit trees.

Other solitary bees

There are over 200 species of solitary bees in the UK. They are called solitary bees as they do not live in social colonies. Among this group is the Leaf-cutter bees, which is an important pollinating group for a variety of fruits, vegetables and other plants including wild flowers. Leaf-cutter bees may nest in a variety of places, such as dead wood, hollow stems, cavities in walls and occasionally in the soil. These bees are widespread and commonly found in gardens.

One of the most common Leaf-cutter bee is the Patchwork Leaf-cutter *Megachile centuncularis*. Patchwork Leaf-cutters look similar to honey bees. They are probably best known for cutting semi-circular pieces out of Rose and Wisteria leaves, that they take to the nest. The bee then glues the pieces of leaf together to build cells for their eggs in which their young grow safely. Within each cell the egg is given a supply of pollen from a variety of flowers. The hatched larvae pupate into adults in autumn and hibernate in their cells over winter.

The miners

If you find a small hole in your lawn surrounded by a mound of excavated earth, it could be the home of a mining bee. These solitary bees nest in the ground and are part of the Andrena genus; a 67-strong group of bees ranging from 5-7mm long.

There are two mining bees you are most likely to see:

The Tawny mining bee *Andrena fulva* is a honeybee-sized ginger species with a thick orange coat and a black face. It feeds on shrubs ranging from Willow, Hawthorn and Blackthorn to fruit trees and Maples, and loves Dandelions. Tawny mining bees are found in a wide variety of habitats, including parks and gardens. They prefer sunny short turf and light soils that are easy to dig. If there is an area of exposed soil or a bare bank you are likely to see one.

The Ashy mining bee *Andrena cineraria* is a distinctive species, black and white in colour. It can be found in moorland, open woodland, coastal grassland, cliffs and quarries. Some of their favourite food plants include Willow, Blackthorn, Gorse, Buttercups and fruit trees.

The honeybees

There is just one species of honeybee in the UK, *Apis mellifera*. Honeybees have been domesticated for centuries and it is rare to find a truly wild colony. They live in hives of up to 20,000 individuals and they like open flowers they can easily reach with their short tongues.

A subspecies of the honeybee is the European Dark bee (*Apis mellifera mellifera*). They are large for honeybees but still have short tongues. Traditionally they were called the German Dark bee, and in the UK the Black bee, a common name derived from their brown-black colour. These bees were thought extinct in the UK but have been rediscovered in several locations. Their darker colour and thicker coats are believed to make them better adapted to cold weather than the ordinary honeybee. Following the spread of honeybee colony collapses, and general population decline, these surviving Black bee populations are of great interest as breeding stock to introduce more disease and cold resistance into the wider honeybee population.

Attempts to conserve and help the spread of Black bees has been lead in West Cornwall by the Blacks Cornish Bees project, with colonies established on the Lizard, at Godolphin House and at Heligan gardens.

The hoverflies

Alongside bees, another important pollinating group is the similar looking hoverflies. Although hoverflies look like bees or wasps, they are in fact flies and do not sting. They mimic bees and wasps to out-smart predators. It has been shown that they are as important as bees for pollination and consume roughly 20% of aphid pests.

There are about 250 different hoverfly species in Britain. You can generally see plenty of adults on flowers throughout spring, summer and autumn. Hoverfly larvae all have different feeding habits. They may eat plants, feed on rotting wood and fungi, attack bulbs or parasitise other insects.

Butterflies and moths

Unlike the bees or hoverflies, butterflies and moths are long tongued pollinators so they can feed on tubular flowers with nectaries hidden deep, such as Foxglove, Penstemon and Honeysuckle. As well as pollinating, they are vital for the food chain and they provide lots of protein for birds. And, of course, there can be few comparable sources of delight in the garden to the duelling confetti of butterflies dancing on a summer day.

The UK has 59 species of butterfly – 57 resident and two regular migrants, the Painted Lady and Clouded Yellow. Like other insects, butterflies have very different juvenile forms than adults. They are different not only in appearance but in lifestyle too. Only the juvenile caterpillars feed, the adults are short lived and focused on breeding. During adulthood they survive on nectar.

Five species of UK butterfly have become extinct in the last 150 years. These are the Mazarine Blue, Large Tortoiseshell, Black-veined White, Large Copper and Large Blue. (Large Blue was successfully reintroduced to Britain in 1992). Because they are so beautiful, people understandably want to avoid more losses and to help butterflies flourish in their gardens. To do this we have to provide three things:

To be a butterfly haven it is good that a garden is both rich in flowers for the adults and also in the food plants the caterpillars need. Caterpillars are often selective feeders, so availability of the right plants is critical. Fortunately, since the butterfly is very mobile, you don't need to provide all the food plants in one garden. The fertilised mother will hunt in the neighbourhood to find the right plant to lay her eggs. She can easily fly several miles in a day. Therefore, although Nettles are important caterpillar plants, you do not have to grow them yourself, it may be better to put the energy into encouraging your local council and landowners not to be too tidy and to leave some wild patches in your area. More butterflies for everyone that way.

The cocoon

After the caterpillars have fed and built up enough reserves, something remarkable happens – they form cocoons. Cocoons provide a protective coat for an extraordinary transformation. Sheltered inside, the entire being of the larva that was, falls apart into a structureless soup; it looks like decay and total disaster, but nothing could be further from the truth. Somewhere in this chaotic mass are a few very special cells, called imaginal cells; they have the same DNA as the larvae but somehow they hold a different vision of how to organise and how to live. Slowly these cells realise their vision and organise the soup into an entirely different form – the adult becomes ready to emerge as a beautiful soaring creature that brings joy to us and helps others to live by pollinating.

Moths

Moths have similar life cycles but are much more diverse than butterflies, with over 2,500 species in Britain. Since 1914 there have been 56 moth extinctions. Six of these have since recolonised or been re-found. Probably because they fly at night and hide their beauty from us, gardening for moths seems less common than for butterflies. Even so, the abundance of the UK's larger moths has crashed and they deserve our help.

Both adult moths and their caterpillars are food for a wide

variety of wildlife, including other insects, spiders, frogs, toads, lizards, shrews, hedgehogs, bats and birds. Many birds eat both adult moths and their caterpillars, but the caterpillars are especially important for feeding their young. Many of our favourite garden birds rely on caterpillars to rear their nestlings, with our Blue Tit chicks alone needing an estimated 35 billion a year. Night-flying moths also form a major part of the diet of bats.

Many of the declining moth species, like the Burnished Brass and Oak Hook-tip, live in gardens and hedges. Therefore, everyone is able to help in their conservation. The way we all manage our gardens can make a big difference to their survival. Even better, making a difference can be simple, too much tidiness is not good for wildlife, and nor is too much concrete, decking and gravel.

Moths and their caterpillars like fallen leaves, old stems and other plant debris to help them hide from predators, and especially to provide suitable places to spend the winter. If you can bear it, delay cutting back old plants until the spring, rather than doing it in the autumn, and just generally let things be. If you have hedges, limit the amount of trimming. If you want your garden to look tidy, try leaving some old plant material out of sight. Many moth caterpillars feed on the native plants we consider weeds, so tolerating some weeds and long grass in your garden is also very beneficial.

Pesticides and herbicides are harmful to moths or the plants on which their caterpillars feed. Organic gardening is better for all wildlife, but if you can't go completely organic, cutting down on the use of chemicals as much as possible will help. Buying organic food can also be valuable as it will encourage more farmers to reduce the use of poisons.

You can also help moths by the choice of plants you grow in

your garden. Having a wide variety of plants is the key – diversity supports diversity. It is good to have a mix of large and small flowering plants plus a few shrubs, and a small tree if you have room. Lots of flowers with plenty of nectar will provide a good source of food for adult moths, the same flowers will also attract more butterflies, while specific plants can provide the necessary food for caterpillars. Some flowers have more available nectar than others, so by choosing the best plants you can make your garden a better feeding station.

Generally, older varieties and less hybridised species tend to have more nectar. Double flowers are harder for pollinators to feed from, so give preference to varieties with simple, single flowers. As different species of moth and butterfly are feeding at different times of the year, you should aim to have nectar-bearing flowers out in as many months as possible, including early spring and late summer and autumn.

Good plants for supplying nectar in spring include Aubretia, Bluebell, Forget-me-not, Pansy, Primrose and Wallflower. Don't forget that lawns can shelter many flowers too, Clover is particularly good, as are Daisies, Dandelions and Speedwell. The conservation charity, Plantlife, have a campaign called 'No Mow May' encouraging us to leave a short gap for lawn flowers to grow at the start of summer as a boost to the flowers and their pollinators. As they tell us; every flower counts.

For late summer and autumn nectar, plant Buddleia, French Marigold, Ice Plant, Knapweed, Lavender, Marjoram, Michaelmas Daisy, Sage, Red Valerian, Scabious and Thyme. Ivy is especially good for autumn flying moths, as it flowers in October and November.

Night-scented plants are particularly valuable for moths. These include summer flowering Jasmine, Honeysuckle, Evening Primrose, Sweet Rocket and Night-scented Stock. Tobacco plants, commonly sold as summer bedding plants, can also be good but you need to look for the original species *Nicotiana alata*, as modern varieties have lost much of their scent. The fashionable *Nicotiana sylvestris* is a tall white form that is very attractive to moths, but unfortunately its tubular flowers are too long for resident British moths to actually reach the nectar.

Luckily an adult moth may take nectar from many types of flowers, which do not need to be native species. However, if you plant some native species, or close relatives, these are more likely to also supply suitable food for the caterpillars.

A garden with a greater variety of plants is likely to provide a home for more types of moth. The caterpillars of many species eat the leaves of native trees, especially Willow, Birch and Oak, so if your garden has these trees nearby you will probably get the adult moths visiting your garden for nectar. Even if the caterpillars don't live in your garden, it doesn't matter; again you could encourage your local council or landowners to preserve local patches of wild native trees – Hawthorn and Willow are highly important.

Also, for a boundary hedge, you can use a mixture of native species, particularly Hawthorn, Blackthorn, Hazel, Beech, Spindle and Privet. Fruit trees and fruit bushes are also good, especially Apple, Plum, Cherry and Currant. If there is a wall or fence for climbers then do plant them, the best choices are Roses, native Honeysuckle (*Lonicera*), Clematis, Hop and Ivy.

Many caterpillars eat the leaves and roots of native grasses and plants often considered weeds. It can be a good idea to leave an area with grasses left to grow long in a mix with Docks, Bramble, Plantains, Dandelions and Nettles.

Approaches to wildlife gardening

Added together these individual efforts in gardens will make a huge difference. On average one quarter of the area of a typical city, and half its green space, is private garden. Researchers have calculated that the UK has a total cover of private gardens of roughly 433,000 ha, which is a fifth the size of Wales and comparable to the area of the Norfolk Broads, Exmoor, Dartmoor and the Lake District National Parks added together.

So we gardeners can make a huge contribution to protecting endangered insects. The 'wildlife garden' approach, first popularised by Chris Baines, and subsequently championed by Wildlife Trusts and many others, often means deliberately introducing features that support wildlife – such as ponds and nest boxes, together with planting selected food plants.

An easier and gentler approach has been pioneered and inspired by the Irish 'recovering landscape designer' Mary Reynolds. Mary writes that she grew disenchanted with trying to force gardens to become different to what the land wanted to be, so she began looking at the potential of stepping back, just a little, and letting the garden ecosystem evolve how it wants to. Her idea is bewitchingly simple and echoes the growing interest in rewilding the countryside.

The key is not to try to control what happens, but instead have faith that, after millions of years of evolution, nature will know what to do as long as we get out of the way, and especially stop killing key members of our essential biodiversity. Her idea is to let a patch of garden go its own way with minimal interference, except maybe clearing harmful weeds, but letting long grass and dead stems remain where they can. This patch becomes your part of the Ark movement, providing safe havens for many species. Together, the networked gardens of the Ark movement are providing refuge for a richly distributed nature reserve. Through a website and social media, gardeners encourage each other, share their work and problem solve.

Mary's approach is backed up by the science of garden ecology. The BUGS (Biodiversity and Urban Gardens Study) project was a three-year research study based in Sheffield University, it looked at the significance of urban gardens as habitats and the efficacy of some simple measures for enhancing that biodiversity. Broadly, the researchers found that overall plant diversity and structural complexity were the keys to supporting a wide range of wildlife. Another finding was that some widely promoted wildlife features, such as insect nest boxes, made little difference. Much more important was the presence of nearby large trees and patches of wild vegetation.

Over the fence

The lesson is we should pay attention to what is over the fence, not just within the garden, and encourage local landowners to protect old trees and water bodies in particular. Since the 17th century, Chinese and Japanese garden designers used the technique of borrowed scenery called 'shakkei'. The idea is to integrate visible elements from outside the garden – trees, views and mountains – as part of the composition. Similarly, ecological science shows us that borrowed nearby habitats also play a key role in enriching our garden wildlife.

Does it have to come from here?

It is often said that only native plants are beneficial for wildlife but this is not always true. Even so, gardens are not poor in natives anyway. The Sheffield researchers found that typically UK gardens contained approximately one third native plants (weeds included) and two thirds non-native (alien to the UK) but

119

they felt the difference for wildlife was less important than sometimes argued.

They state:

'Alien status alone is certainly not enough to prevent common garden plants from being fed on by native herbivores and a diverse mix of native and introduced plants is the best solution to support wildlife.'

Other researchers have also found that many insects and birds do not discriminate in where they get their food from and even the much-maligned non-native conifers are valuable for the shelter and refuges they provide. Given the relatively few native evergreen trees we have, we should not overlook the value of useful life-supporting plants wherever they come from, as long as they are not causing other problems.

Birds

As well as helping the arthropods, our gardens are homes, or at least feeding stations, for many larger animals, including the birds. Birds are amongst the best loved members of our garden communities.

Birds have an extraordinary evolutionary history that adds to their wonder. 100 million years ago, giant and ferocious predators, the dinosaurs, may have hunted where your garden is today. They survived on Earth for millions of years until everything changed catastrophically. It is often said that they ruled the Earth, but I suspect 'ruling' was not their thing, they just wanted to get by.

They did get by for millions of years, until 66 million years ago their world was devastated; an asteroid had struck the Earth and everything was on fire. Even the air burned. The skies were turned black by dust and smoke, and sunlight was blocked, causing an 'impact winter'. The world then froze and pushed the dinosaurs further towards extinction. Despite this, and amazingly, there were survivors. Fortunately, long before this devastation, they had diversified into other forms of life. Many were smaller, needing less food and better able to shelter, some had grown feathers and flew to safety. Life finds a way.

The small survivors dispersed across the devastated planet and started creating a new world. Today, remarkably, their descendants sit outside your window and sing sweetly to wake you every morning. The closet living relatives to the bitey dinosaurs are the songbirds in our gardens. Out of unimaginable destruction emerged colour, song and beauty.

Deborah Bird Rose writes of what she learnt from indigenous Australian elders:

'The living world is more complicated, less predictable, more filled with transformations, uncertainty, and fantastic eruptions of life's mysteries than is allowed of in ordinary thought.'

Surely there can be no more fantastic, unpredictable transformation than that the descendants of giant killing predators, emerged from flame and ashes as songbirds! It is almost beyond mythology, but it happened. Our ordinary thought certainly does not begin to get close to these wonders.

Almost as extraordinary as the story of the birds' survival, is the wonder of what they evolved into. Despite the disparaging term 'birdbrain', birds are actually among the most intelligent creatures that share our world. Birds do have smaller brains than we do, but they are packed with neurons, meaning their small brains can have as many nerve cells as us much larger primates.

Songs, the amazing language of birds
The fact that birds sing is an outward sign of that intelligence, as are the complex lives they lead. Not all birds sing. Some, like the

121

f

owls, rely on silence. Yet songbirds make up nearly half of the world's 9,600 bird species.

Songbirds, named for their singing ability, make another type of sound as well – calls rather than songs. Calls perform many different functions – warning, scalding, calling a gathering, courtship and marking a territory. As mentioned previously, scientists believe that call sounds are innate and instinctive, rather like the bark of a dog or the meow of a cat. Songs are much more complex and require much more subtle and prolonged vocalisations, more brain power too. The songs of birds are learned, not innate. Within a couple of months of hatching, fledglings develop a 'subsong' like a baby's first attempt at speech. With practice, the song matures into an adult primary song which takes a year or so. During this learning period, some species will develop a number of songs and calls. House Sparrows have just one simple song; Song Thrushes and Nightingales have several different ones.

Some bird species are also experts at mimicry and will copy many sounds, ranging from other birds to mechanical noises. Starlings are well known for this and other species, such as the Jay, are known to mimic birds of prey, such as Buzzards, to scare off intruders to their territory. This gives an insight into why mimicry is useful.

Most singing takes place during the breeding season, usually in the early morning and late afternoon. This is when they are settled in their territory and are declaring their presence to others.

Can you hear me?

Because bird calls and songs play an important role in their survival and social bonding, birds have to ensure that they can be heard. As previously detailed, researchers believe that one of the reasons why birds perch on high structures is not just for scrutiny of their surroundings, but also to give a good vantage for calling or singing. For males especially, a conspicuous spot is desirable to attract a mate or deter competitors. A few birds, such as Buntings or Sky Larks, sing while flying.

Birds usually do not sing near their nests as this could attract unwanted attention, although a few may sing a quiet whisper song that can be heard only within a few yards. This is because the chicks can hear through their shells and begin their learning even before they hatch.

The collective singing early in the morning is known as the dawn chorus. In high summer it can start as early as 4am. The first birds to wake and sing are usually Blackbirds, Robins and Wrens. A sign of their intelligence is that birds constantly monitor their surroundings and adapt their behaviour. The dawn chorus may be timed to commence before competing sounds build up. It has been found that birds near airports, railway lines or roads may begin to sing earlier and with a different pitch.

The favoured habitat of a bird also affects how and when it sings. Those that prefer low ground in dense vegetation often sing in lower pitch, as low-pitched sounds travel further and are less attenuated by obstacles than are high frequency sounds. The dawn chorus drops in intensity during the breeding season and when the young are being cared for and stops when the breeding season is over.

Although not evolved for us, bird song really is a gift to us and is important. As already detailed, many studies have linked natural sounds, like diverse birdsong and the sound of susurration, to reduced stress. Listening in on the sounds of the garden is a window into a complex and wonderful dimension of nature and can be healing for us too. For this reason, we should be conscious of impacts that threaten the health of birds and their singing patterns. Removing a few local trees can feel insignificant to us but to the local bird population these can be important hubs for their social lives and survival. Another issue is light pollution, which is known to impact on birds' singing behaviour.

Impacts of light pollution

The Robin, for example, is adapted to feed from insects in low dark undergrowth. This bird has large eyes for its size to hunt in low light intensities, so it feeds and sings earlier and later than most other birds. The Robin is often still active and singing through the evening and is almost always the first up in the morning. It is becoming more common for Robins to sing through the night and it is believed that streetlights are keeping them awake and confusing them. This night singing is becoming widespread and they are sometimes mistaken for Nightingales. Night singing of birds is one of the most obvious effects of light pollution.

Research has shown that it is not only birds that suffer from the effects of light pollution, insects also get confused, adding to the pressures on them. People may suffer from light pollution too. Our natural body functions are strongly influenced by the circadian rhythm – the normal pattern of bright days and dark nights. When these signals are disrupted and confused, we may sleep badly and show hormone disruption and a weakened immune system. What is bad for birds and insects is bad for us too.

The International Dark Skies Association was formed by amateur astronomers who found that because of the artificial light in towns and cities, they could no longer pursue their science without travelling far from home.

Over time the Association has collated evidence to support the case for darkness and especially darker skies. They state:

'For most of human history, a spectacular universe of stars and galaxies has been visible in the darkness of the night sky. The dark sky has inspired questions about our universe and our relation to it. The history of scientific discovery, art, literature, astronomy, navigation, exploration, philosophy, and even human curiosity itself would be diminished without our view of the stars. But today, the increasing number of people living on earth and the corresponding increase in inappropriate and unshielded outdoor lighting has resulted in light pollution – a brightening night sky that has obliterated the stars for much of the world's population. Most people must travel far from home, away from the glow of artificial lighting, to experience the awe-inspiring expanse of the Milky Way as our ancestors once knew it.'

Birds of a feather, why do birds flock together?

There are believed to be many benefits to living in a social group as a flock. Firstly, it improves a bird's defences against predators, because a large group of birds is stronger and better protected, and with many eyes on the watch for attack, the flock is far more likely to spot a would-be predator. Also, the predator will find it harder to concentrate on a single victim, and this increases each individual member of the flock's chance of survival. Additionally, multiple movements, especially the whirling flight of flocked birds such as Starlings, confuses attackers.

Flocking whilst flying also enables birds to fly further, using less energy because when the leader bird flaps its wings it creates uplift for the birds behind. Each bird (except the leader) is flying in a slipstream. This enables the entire flock to use less energy and reduces fatigue. Energy conservation is believed to be key to the long journeys made by migratory species.

Roosting

A related question is why do some birds form large communal roosts and other do not? This has been one of the longest standing puzzles of bird ecology. An early theory that distracted us for a long time was that they roost together for warmth. For species that jam together in cavities, warmth might be the main advantage, but scientists are sceptical that this applies to roosting colonies in trees. They argue that the energy spent in returning to roosts every night outweighs the benefits, so they believe there must be other reasons. Only after years of careful monitoring and tracking has an accepted answer for communal roosting emerged.

It seems that roosts are, in fact, places of learning. The birds learn songs from each other and, importantly, tips of where to find the best feeding spots. It has even been shown that 'outsiders' joining a roost more quickly learn about the local territory and where feeding is best. Rather than a 'murder' of Crows, perhaps we should call them a 'school' of Crows.

One reason it took so long for us to understand this is because only recently have we believed that birds are intelligent enough to teach and learn from each other.

Finding our niche

Every living thing survives by developing its own specialisms, what ecologists call its own niche. Niches allow us to avoid too much overlap and competition with others. We see examples in the garden everywhere, from the way that different pollinators access different flowers, to the way that different layers of plant leaves share the sunlight and air between them.

Birds also divide the air into niches, feeding and flying in different strata. Swifts are very specialised feeders, their niche is as hunters of the upper air, feeding on aeroplankton, flying ants and gossamer-riding Money spiders sailing in the wind. Like many airborne specialists, Swifts have developed techniques of flying that use the least energy; they glide rather than fly, their aerodynamic shape lets them use the wind's energy to stay aloft. Martins and Swallows choose lower strata and feed on heavier insects like flies, still way above those birds that find their sustenance from the earth.

Most birds switch from one type of food to another, depending on what is available. They adapt their diet to the seasons, patterns of plant growth and insect behaviour. These adaptations also reflect their niche. The Blackbird, for example, has good foraging skills and can rely on a wide range of foods. It varies its diet of worms, small insects and spiders with fruits and berries and kitchen scraps, pond life and even mice. The Song Thrush is another adaptable feeder that has a unique talent of breaking open snail shells by bashing them on hard surfaces. Winter is a time of shortage, a time when birds have to diversify their diets, omnivores like Carrion Crows, Jays and Magpies may even resort to feeding on smaller birds.

Pecking orders

There are two different perspectives on the term 'pecking order'. The first comes from observation of patterns of hierarchy and dominance amongst flocks, especially of chickens kept in captivity. In these artificially constrained situations, the most dominant and aggressive birds are the first to feed. Even though the food supply is effectively limitless, the birds don't know it, so they bully each other to get first dibs. This is the form of behaviour that draws parallels with human 'hierarchies'.

Another, more gentle, pecking order is seen in gardens every morning when birds come to feed on the lawn or the bird feeder. Several things determine what happens and when. Firstly and obviously, which bird gets up first, or which one is just too tired. This probably also reflects how hungry the birds are, when they last fed and how much energy they lost through the night keeping warm. Secondly, preferred food is a factor – no point in hunting flying insects very early before the day has warmed enough to tempt them into flight. Early feeders therefore tend to be those who hunt on lawns, in undergrowth, or the berry feeders. Then there is an issue of how confident the birds are and when they feel safe enough to emerge from shelter. This in turns depends on how well they know you, your movements and the behaviour of local cats and other disturbances such as deliveries. Altogether the result is often a daily pattern that becomes predictable.

From your kitchen window you can enjoy these patterns unfolding, watch the dance and maybe even get to know the individuals. Typically in the UK, as already stated, Robins are up and feeding first because as birds of dense undergrowth they have good twilight vision. Then come the Blackbirds and Sparrows, Tits, and later larger birds like Pigeons and Magpies drop in. On a bird feeder, competition and dominance between species visibly plays out. The stronger and more aggressive win an early place. Smaller birds must be agile and wait their turn.

Becoming invisible
To get the most enjoyment from birds in your garden, there is a skill to learn – the skill of getting them used to your presence. Jon Young explains that with practice we can reduce our 'sphere of disturbance' and increase our 'invisibility'. This may involve wearing subdued colours, making less noise, not wearing strong

scents and avoiding sudden moves. It also helps to develop regular daily patterns – the birds will not waste energy hiding from something they know is not a threat. If you go outside at similar times each day, and keep to habits, more creatures will be confident enough to go about their daily activities with similar regularity.

Joe Harkness and Simon Barnes, and many other experts in environmental education, all agree that a great asset is a 'sit spot', somewhere you can visit daily to base your nature observations from. Not only does this acclimatise the animals to you and your patterns, it gets you in a habit of training your observation skills. Another tip Joe Harkness recommends is what he describes as 'walking like a fox' – avoiding rushed or jerky movements. Take small steps and pause after each one, let the birds get used to your movement, rest, observe what is happening and step slowly again – if you see no startled behaviour, all is well. Not only do the birds not hide when you are not scaring them, but they also make fewer alarm calls, so other wildlife is less wary also.

In lockdown, because our territory has had to shrink, it makes sense to get more richness from the spaces we can still access. Use this time to work out your senses, practise invisibility and build more trust with your neighbouring wildlife families.

Some birds will gain confidence faster than others. All the creatures that live alongside us reveal their evolutionary history in their behaviour. Why are Robins such tame and confident birds? Scientists believe that Robins evolved to follow ground foraging animals through woodland to feed off of the insects that they disturbed. So rustling, grunting and digging about are no worry to them. To the Robins, when you dig the garden, you are just a funny looking Wild Boar or an Aurochs in pants (that is if you bother with pants in lockdown).

The largest animals

We can put the largest garden animals into two categories; there are the ones that fit into a small garden ecosystem and then there are the bigger ones that do not fit at all. These are usually not bounded by your garden plot, they are too large to survive in a small space, they are passing visitors that may stop by for a meal at most. These largest of garden creatures are reminders that like the creatures in them, our gardens are not isolated, they are part of a network. Our garden boundaries are porous and fences are no obstacle to many animals. Our neighbours come and go regularly and may include some great oddities amongst them.

Moles, the channel diggers

Moles are not the oddest by any means; they are gentle creatures perfectly adapted to an underground life. They have arms designed for digging, a sleek velvet fur to streamline their movement through the soil and an ability to survive in low oxygen conditions. Mostly they feed on earthworms and other soil insects and they do not harm plants directly. In fact, they do the plants good by improving drainage – the channels they make in the soil are much larger than worms can create, adding to aeration and drainage and potentially reducing flooding and keeping soils healthy. Although they are sometimes regarded as garden pests, the only real issue they create is to deposit freshly dug soil on the surface, where it can look unsightly and lead to weed germination. Usually this only matters on pristine turf, if it matters at all.

Squirrels, the naughty ones

Squirrels are good examples of animals for whom no fences matter. These small tree living rodents mostly live off fruits, nuts and shoots. They are the closest UK relative of the American chipmunks and Prairie dogs. Scientists studying Prairie dogs have found that they have an amazingly evolved language capability, and it has even been possible to determine what they are saying to each other. The Prairie dogs can, it seems, warn each other of people approaching, and they can even describe what the people are wearing and whether they are carrying guns. Chipmunks, too, are known to communicate by calls and body language.

Maybe the squirrels also have something of this ability? We don't know, but we do know that they are intelligent and very communicative. Squirrels will scold any approaching threats. They also use calls and their tails and body language to communicate. For example, they may point out a potential danger to each other using their tails like a pointing finger. Unlike Prairie dogs we believe that they are making instinctive sounds, calls that they can only understand intuitively. So far no one has found they have language subtle enough to describe us. . . so far, anyway. The right research is yet to be done. Maybe they do have hidden depths to their communication and we just haven't decoded it yet. Next time you go into the garden and hear a chattering or see a tail pointing, wonder who is gossiping about you. Maybe saying, "Check out the Aurochs with no pants on!"

Grey squirrels fall firmly in the category of wildlife that we are told 'must be controlled'. Uncontrolled they are disliked for damaging trees by stripping bark, and affecting populations of the cuter Red squirrels, songbirds and Dormice. They do this by competing for food and possibly they spread disease. We are told, therefore, to put them on the naughty list. Not that they care. You can almost hear them calling, "Whatever!"

Yet this does not mean they do no good in the garden. Squirrels, like Jays, are important for carrying and burying heavy seeds like acorns. They plant new woodlands for us. Squirrels are also important for the joy they bring. For many of us they are the only wild mammals we see with any regularity, it is a happy bonus that they are so bold and entertaining to watch. Like many naughty moments it is hard not to crack a smile at their antics.

Hedgehogs, the nice ones

The hedgehog is viewed in stark contrast to the squirrel, it seems it can do nothing wrong and is on everyone's nice list. Rarely seen and declining in numbers, the hedgehog is a valuable slug eater and is welcome for it in every garden. Accordingly, lots of people are keen to know how best to accommodate these endearing visitors.

Fortunately, to make a garden attractive for hedgehogs is not demanding. You do not need to buy an artificial hedgehog home, just leave areas of the garden 'wild', with piles of leaf litter and logs. These make an attractive nest as well as a home for the slugs, bugs, and beetles that hedgehogs like to eat. If you have a resident hedgehog and no rats, you can put out food like tinned dog or cat food, and crushed dog or cat biscuits, but fish and milk are not suitable. As with much of our garden wildlife, access to fresh water is important, but open water can present a risk of drowning, so bricks and 'ramps' at the side of ponds give important escape routes.

Slug pellets can poison hedgehogs and should be avoided. If you believe you have to use them, place them somewhere inaccessible to the hedgehogs. Later I return to the vexed question of living with slugs – take heart, there are options.

Garden rodents

Small rodents like mice, voles and shrews are mostly nocturnal – you may not even know they are in the garden until you find a dead one, thanks to the local cats probably, or when you see damage from them. Otherwise the best signs are tracks and small holes amongst long grass or at the base of dense hedges.

Four species of mice and voles are common in UK gardens. The Wood mouse, *Apodemus sylvestris*, the Short-tailed vole, *Microtus agrestis*, and the Bank vole, *Myodes glareolus*, are widely distributed. The Yellow-necked Field mouse, *Apodemus flavicollis*, mainly occurs in southern England and Wales. Additional evidence that they are near and hungry could be gnaw marks on stems and stored fruits and vegetables.

Most of the time the population levels are probably low and they will do little harm, but when they are struggling for food, they can and will feed on a wide range of plants. Holes may be seen in the soil where mice or voles have dug down to feed on bulbs, corms or germinating seeds. Remnants of seedlings may be scattered on the soil surface. Soft areas in a lawn with small heaps of soil on the surface are likely to be due to voles tunnelling just beneath the surface. Field mice sometimes bite off fruits before they are ripe and leave them in small heaps among the plants.

Mice and voles may also eat freshly sown seeds of peas, beans and Sweet corn and kill seedling plants by grazing on the foliage. In cold weather, Field mice often enter greenhouses and cold frames, where they can destroy many seedlings overnight. Crocus corms and Tulip bulbs are often eaten, especially soon after planting, but established bulbs and corms are less susceptible.

Voles sometimes eat the bark of woody plants, particularly in winter when other vegetation is frozen. Fitting young or newly planted trees with tree guards can help reduce this damage. To reduce damage by these animals, wherever possible use barriers and secure storage rather than killing them.

Mice and voles remain active all year round. The breeding season is between spring and autumn, when the young are born underground in nests made of dry grass. Rodents aren't generally the most popular, but they are a valuable part of the food chain. Aiming to keep a balance will help you build the richest diversity in your garden, and other animals will help you. Cats and foxes, owls and other birds of prey, and sometimes even Crows, Jays and Magpies will feed on rodents. When times get hard for the mice and they become pests, times gets hard for the others, too, and they will step up the hunting, after millions of years of finding a balance, nature usually has a solution to excess.

Bats, the night patrollers

There are eighteen species of bat in Britain. The most commonly seen is the smallest. It has a charming name, the Pipistrelle. Although it weighs only about 5g, a Pipistrelle bat can eat thousands of insects every night.

British bats are divided into two groups. The Earlet bats have long ears through which they receive their echo signals. Two species are known as Horseshoe bats. The Greater and Lesser Horseshoe bats have a horseshoe-shaped growth on the nose. As the Horseshoe bat flies, it emits ultrasonic squeaks through its nose. It can move its nose parts to direct the sounds. At the same time the bat waggles its ears backwards and forwards to receive the echoes.

Bats are difficult to identify in flight but the Pipistrelle can usually be recognised by its small size, and in good light the Long-eared bat's ears may be spotted. British bats eat lots of insects, therefore they are valuable pest controllers. Generally anything good for nocturnal insects is good for bats too.

Echo location, seeing with the ears

Although bats have reasonable eyesight, they hunt their prey by using a form of radar called echolocation. As the bat flies, it emits a series of ultrasonic squeaks that are usually out of range of human hearing. As these sound waves come into contact with objects along the flight line they bounce echoes back to the bat's receiving organs, allowing bats to avoid obstacles and catch their prey. People too can practise a basic form of echolocation. By clapping or bashing sticks on hard surfaces, we can tell if we are in an enclosed space, and roughly how big it is. Some people with longterm sight loss have developed highly attuned skills in echolocation.

As well as gardens, bats live in woodlands, wetlands, and often in derelict buildings. They are highly sensitive to disturbance, habitat loss and destruction of their flying routes. The bats' dependence on undisturbed habitats and high insect numbers makes them good indicators of overall biodiversity health. Bats have suffered huge declines in the last century and now have high levels of protection. New developments are required by law to avoid damaging their bat roosts.

Like most wildlife, bats need access to clean fresh water. If your garden is too small for a pond, there may be streams nearby that they depend on. You can help ensure that these important resources are in good condition by checking them for signs of pollution and informing your local authority of problems.

The very largest garden animals

The largest animals that commonly visit gardens in the UK are usually badgers, foxes and deer, although bizarre rarities sometimes pop up too. In 2020 a wallaby was sighted several times in St Blazey, Cornwall, and several instances of llama drama have occurred in my small Cornish town, one involving damage to a car. These exotic animals are almost certainly escapees from private collections. Wallabies may soon become a more common garden visitor, recently scientists have mapped nearly 100 confirmed sightings of wild living wallabies in the UK. It seems that they are coping with our climate and naturalising.

Badgers

Badgers are truly native in the UK. They are omnivores from the family that includes otters, polecats, weasels and wolverines. Badgers mainly eat earthworms and insects, and may also eat small mammals and birds, as well as fruit and nuts. Badgers are natural diggers so they can cause significant damage to gardens and lawns when foraging. Robins love them, of course – next best thing to a Wild Boar or an Aurochs.

Along with foxes, there has been a big growth in urban badger populations. Towns have become safer than the countryside for them.

Deer

Aside from llamas and wallabies, deer are the largest free-roaming browsing animals in the UK. Large browsing animals like deer or wallabies do not really belong in gardens, but unfortunately they neither know that or care.

Several species of deer, especially Roe and Muntjac, regularly visit UK gardens and cause severe damage to a wide range of plants. They will strip flowers, foliage and also tree bark. If you see what looks like a weird Alsation dog with horns skittering around, barking and eating your Roses, it will be a Muntjac deer, another escapee from private collections. They established in the wild in the early 1800s.

Like foxes, as the countryside becomes more hostile to them, urban living becomes attractive enough to deer for them to overcome their shyness. Also, due to the absence of natural predators, deer populations are booming and they disperse wherever they can to reduce competition for food. Even if they visit your garden for a meal, odds are high that they will not be living there but in nearby woodland. Mostly deer forage at night, so you may rarely see them as much as the damage they do.

You may not come to love the deer, or llamas, that visit, but they are remarkable animals to have skittering past our windows. They remind us again that our gardens are not isolated, but are one small part of the wider ecosystem, special places for us to meet a world's wonders. Whether we can be as relaxed about the wild cat escapees remains to be seen.

Reptiles

Our cold and wet climate means that there are few reptiles common in our gardens.

As cold-blooded animals, they are most often seen when sun bathing and basking in warm and dry places. They like rocks and walls as they retain the sun's heat. They also like compost heaps that generate heat as the vegetation rots. Some reptiles have thermoreceptors – heat sensing organs that enable them to identify the warmest spots to shelter, and to hunt their prey.

Slow worms

Slow worms are not small snakes but legless lizards, which for anyone with a phobia may be a subtle difference, but they are harmless and graceful creatures. Adult slow worms grow to about 30cm in length. Unlike a snake, the slow worm has eyelids that blink regularly and smooth, shiny scales with a polished, metallic appearance. The overall body colour is a shiny grey-brown, and they may have bluish lines or spots which helps their camouflage.

Slow worms need heat from sunlight and thick vegetation to shelter in. They frequently bask on walls and stone or log piles.

Even so they are shy and rarely seen in the open during daylight, because they have many predators – birds, hedgehogs, badgers, and domestic cats all will attack them. They have evolved a remarkable defensive tactic – they can shed and regrow their tails. This is presumed to distract the attackers while the slow worm escapes back to cover.

At dusk they emerge from their shelter to hunt for slugs, worms, spiders and various other insects. They can live for 20 years or more, so they may have been long term residents in your garden – they will know well where to hunt and where to shelter. They know the garden better than you do.

Grass snakes

The Grass snake is Britain's longest snake, with large females sometimes reaching up to 1.5m in length, so they can look scary. Fortunately, they are shy and not venomous. They rarely bite people and usually dive for cover when they detect you approaching.

Grass snakes are usually olive green with black bars along the flanks and black dots on the side. They are most common in meadows or woodland edges, particularly near ponds. Frogs, toads and newts are their favourite food but they will also take fish, small mammals and birds.

Grass snakes are the UK's only egg-laying snake. They normally lay their eggs in a sheltered location within rotting vegetation. Compost heaps are a popular choice because of the warmth they generate. This is where you are most likely to find them as a garden visitor. Up to 40 eggs may be laid by the Grass snake and the mother incubates them until they hatch in late summer or early autumn. Only a few of the young will reach adulthood, with many lost to predators such as Herons, birds of prey, Pheasants and even hedgehogs.

Like most cold-blooded animals, Grass snakes spend the winter in hibernation, using places like compost heaps, rabbit warrens and fallen trees. In summer they may be spotted basking in sun near water or even swimming.

Adders, the only other large snake in Britain, are much less likely to be found in gardens. They prefer heathland or woodland, so you are more likely to encounter them out on a walk, although they are also very shy and will retreat rather than meet you.

Amphibians

Amphibians and reptiles are frequently grouped together, but reptiles mainly live and lay their eggs on the land, while amphibians can live both on land and in water, usually needing water to reproduce. Amphibians breath through their moist skins and this can make them very susceptible to pollution. They are therefore good indicators of habitat quality.

Frogs

Frogs are one of most familiar amphibians we get to see. The tadpoles of the Common frog are the first foray into the magical world of nature for many children, and many of us never lose our fondness for frogs.

People can feel unsure about telling the difference between frogs and toads, but they really are very distinctive from each other. Frogs have smooth, dark patchy skin, long stripey hind legs, webbed feet and dark eye bands. They are smaller than toads, only about 10cm long. Most are brown, olive green or grey and they can adapt their skin colour to blend with their surroundings.

Although they are amphibian and mate and raise their young in water, they can be found even in gardens without ponds, so you can support them even if you don't have a water feature. Frogs do not like strong sun so they will gravitate to shaded spots, behind walls, in logs and stone piles and under planters. They are another joyful excuse for being less tidy.

Frogs are valuable pest controllers as they eat flies, worms, snails and slugs, mostly at night. During winter they hibernate under rocks, in compost heaps, or even buried in mud underwater. Even in winter they may come out in mild spells to forage for food.

The adults breed in early spring, spawning in shallow water, ditches, ponds and even large puddles. The tadpoles are black when they hatch and they eat algae. After about 4 months the tadpoles lose their tails, grow legs and as small froglets they start exploring, feeding and starting their life as adults. In early summer you may spot the tiny froglets scrambling through the garden. It's time to be extra mindful about where you and your pets venture.

Toads

While frogs are sleek and agile, toads are bigger and more lumbering. They walk rather than hop and have broader, squat bodies and warty skin that varies from dark brown, grey and olive green to sand-coloured. They are widespread in Britain and although you may see them in the spring or summer daytime after rain, they usually keep to shelter in damp shady areas, venturing out at night.

Toads hibernate during the winter in deep leaf litter, log piles and in shallow burrows that they have excavated. They eat insects, larvae, spiders, slugs and worms and larger toads may eat slow worms, small Grass snakes and Harvest mice. Like frogs, they will benefit from you leaving wilder patches in the garden.

Toads are normally solitary creatures, but during spring, from early February through to early April (depending on the weather), they will join with hundreds of other toads to migrate to their ancestral breeding ponds, crossing anything in their path. These migrations are usually during a run of warm, wet nights (particularly after or during rain).

Common toads tend to live away from water, except when mating. Whereas frogs are happy with shallow ponds, toads need bigger, deeper bodies of water. Suitable spots are increasingly rare and they must travel further to get where they need to go. They face more obstacles, like roads and housing estates, and this can lead to a distressing annual toll of road deaths. For hours and hours, night after night, they can keep coming. Toad crossing patrols are often rallied to help reduce the death toll.

Toads can live 10-12 years so they may be long term residents in your garden. They produce an irritant in their skin to deter predators, so if your pet attacks or licks them, they can be made ill.

Newts

Newts are the UK representatives of the salamander family. It is believed that the Greeks named salamanders Fire Lizards because they often found them in stacks of firewood. Newts are endangered species and are protected by law. The places they rely on in the countryside – ponds, streams and water bodies free from pollution – are disappearing, so gardens have become important refuges for them.

Amphibians are easily damaged by chemicals which enter their bodies through their moist skins. As amazing creatures, valuable pest control and part of the food chain, they give us another reason to leave the poisons in the garden centre and to welcome the messy nature of nature in our gardens. If you find these shy creatures, try not to handle them too much as even chemicals on our skins can harm them.

Common newts breed and spawn in ponds and ditches, but in late summer they often leave the water and shelter in cool damp spots, under logs or rock piles. They eat worms, insects and even tadpoles. Palmate and Crested newts are the other two widespread British newt species, they look different to the Common newt, but have very similar behaviour and feeding habits.

If you don't have room for a pond, they give another reason to champion the health of local water bodies and keep ditches free of hazards and pollutants.

The world they live in

Having now met the garden animals of different sizes, I would like to look at the habitat and the elements that constitute the garden environment.

Chapter 5

Oh the Wind and Rain

The living members of the garden are not the only sources of beauty, wonder and enchantment. We should also recognise the contribution that weather and skies make to our lives. Our gardens are where we meet the elements as well as meeting wildlife.

The classical elements

The 'classical elements' is the term given to describe the ancient Greek concept that earth, water, air, fire, and aether, were primary substances that in their combinations and interplay, create the complexity of all matter. This philosophy was related to the parallel belief that the human body health and temperaments depended on four humours – yellow bile, black bile, blood, and phlegm. So, they concluded, nature's body in turn was made up of four elements – earth, air, fire and water.

These early Greek philosophers, especially Aristotle, greatly influenced European thinking that accepted the idea that these four elements, weaved in varying proportions, make up the world. Other cultures with other philosophies, saw things differently. In Asian natural philosophy, the idea of five elements is more typical. These are named wood, fire, earth, metal and water, though they are sometimes described more as energies rather than as types of material.

A few years ago I was lucky enough to attend a talk by the late Bob Duggan, founder of the Tai Sophia Institute. Bob was an acupuncturist and he explained to me that acupuncturists often adhered to the Eastern cosmology that favoured 'fives' in contrast, he claimed, to herbalists who tended to work with the Western philosophy of 'fours'. At one point he referred to the five seasons and my ears pricked up. I will talk more of this later but in essence he explained that dividing the year into four or five was not a given, but influenced by a philosophy too.

Modern science has superseded the idea of the four classical elements. Now we know that atoms of more than a hundred chemical elements, like iron, zinc, carbon and nitrogen, all combine to make the physical world, thanks to assembly processes such as those managed by plants and bacteria. These elements form chemical compounds and mixtures, and under different temperatures and pressures, these compounds can adopt different states.

States of matter

The most common states of matter – solid, liquid, gas and plasma – can be argued to approximate to the classical elements of earth, water, air and fire. These states are due to the behaviour of the different compounds at varying energy levels. It gives us a parallel to ancient thinking, but in modern understanding we have no contemporary cosmology of 'elements' to fit them in.

The air we breath

I would like to begin this exploration of the garden elements, that are also ecosystems and living places, by considering the air above – what lives there and what do they do for us?

144

Clouds and trees are fractal shapes.

Mosses are also fractal shapes.

Wistman's Wood; the temperate rainforest.

Hart's-tongue fern.

Fungi and
epiphytes.

Fungi are not plants or animals.

Ants patrol
and protect.

Compositae are lots
of small flowers
jammed together.

Ginkgo leaf
and hoverfly.

Butterflies need our help.

Butterfly on lichen.

Dusts make sunsets more colourful.

Frondescence.

Clock and compass from gathered leaves, by Diana Heyne.

A mandala by Susan Warner.

A mandala by
Susan Warner
within its forest
setting.

Another amazing
mandala by Susan
Warner.

School in a Wood.

The gardens of Eden Project today.

The aerial world is a living ecosystem

Although it is hard for us to recognise that what appears to be an empty void is a vibrant living place, the air above is not empty, it is teeming with life and is one of the most important ecosystems on our planet. The air is like a gaseous ocean, full of biodiversity and resources that sustain all life. Alongside the gases and vapours and fine dusts there are swarms of living beings.

Some of this biodiversity of the air – bats, birds and butterflies – come close enough to enrich our daily lives, but most of those that live above are far beyond our perception, too far and too small to be seen. We can't see them but they live in such abundance that they support many of the things we can see. Without these small things, the big things could not survive.

Aeroplankton

The very smallest of the aerial swarms is known as the aeroplankton. These include tiny flying arthropods, like Money spiders lofted high by silken thread parachutes, gnats, thrips and aphids, and wind-carried spores and seeds. Just one square metre of air may contain millions of these living organisms – a silent multitude that feeds birds, bats, larger flying insects and carries life to new places.

The wonder of dust

Migrating birds and pollinators are not the only wonders that the distant deserts send us. Every year huge quantities of dust join the winds from the Sahara and voyage across the world. Global dust transfers are estimated at 1000-5000 million tons per year of which 60-200 million tons come from the Sahara alone, travelling to Europe, Asia and the Americas.

This dust brings three blessings. First, the particles act as nuclei for rain to form; you may have sometimes seen reddish

g

streaks on your car after rain. This is a sign that the Saharan desert has come to you. Paradoxically, dust from the deserts brings rain to earth, but not in its homeland, it can only do this when it joins air that is moist enough for water to condense. The second gift the deserts give is fertility; falling to earth, the dusts add nutrients to the soils they join. It has been shown that without this gift of fertility, the Amazon forest would be unable to survive. The third gift of the deserts is beauty; Because of light refraction, dusts in the air make the colours of sunsets more intense and daytime skies bluer.

Give thanks for the distant deserts and the gifts they send us.

Air in movement – the weather

An essential quality of air is that it is in constant movement and it is this movement that brings much of our experience of the weather. The energy that creates this air movement comes from the sun. The essential cause is that the sun's energy is not evenly spread over the Earth. Uneven heating causes some air to expand and move. This drives the wind and rain.

The regions that receive more sunlight and heat, warm more and warm faster. The tropics experience less seasonal variation in sunlight than we do. Tropical air, rich in moisture, warms, becomes less dense, and rises. As this air reaches the upper levels of the atmosphere, it cools again. Water molecules condense to form clouds and fall as rain. Warm air rising from the Earth's surface pushes the air mass away from the equator, and it travels towards the poles.

If this warming was the only influence, this cycle would move water and air along a simple and predictable route from the equator to the poles. However, this does not happen as other things interfere and create the prevailing weather patterns that we see.

The Earth's spin is one of the main factors that disrupts this simple model and creates three belts of circulating air. Air circulates from the tropics to regions approximately 30° north and south, where the air masses cool again and sink. This belt of air circulation is referred to as a Hadley cell, after George Hadley, who first described it. Two additional belts of circulating air exist in the temperate latitudes (between 30° and 60°) and near the poles (between 60° and 90°).

The sinking air mass at 30° has two important consequences: It diverts and directs the flow of air moisture in a way that leads to the formation of arid climates and deserts, and drives the circulation of air north and south of the tropics. As warm air rises in the tropics, cool air is drawn from surrounding areas to fill the void. This creates the trade winds that blow in subtropical regions. Winds blowing toward the equator are deflected to the west, creating the easterly trade winds (winds that blow from east to west).

In temperate zones like the UK, where the wind blows towards the poles, the spin of the Earth deflects them towards the east, with prevailing westerlies (blowing from west to east) dictating most of our weather patterns.

Just as the Earth's rotation creates the prevailing winds by affecting the air currents, it also creates currents within the oceans. Waters near the equator also flow from east to west. As in the atmosphere, the spin of the planet causes this water to be deflected away from the equator (northward in the Northern Hemisphere, southward in the Southern Hemisphere). This creates a rotational current within the oceans. The currents of water coming from the equator are warm, of course, and we call this the Gulf Stream. Reaching north, these warmer waters create milder conditions that let tender plants survive in places like the Isles of Scilly.

As water reaches the poles, it cools and sinks. Prevailing winds in northern and southern latitudes create cold-water surface currents that flow back towards the equator along the west coast of continents.

This combination of oceanic and atmospheric circulation distributes heat and moisture and controls our global climate. It plays an important role in creating our familiar seasonal changes. In the Northern Hemisphere, where land masses are more concentrated, these seasonal changes will include significant changes in temperature. In the Southern Hemisphere, where large land masses are located nearer to the equator and the majority of the Earth's surface is covered with water, seasonal cycles are reflected more in the presence and absence of rain rather than major swings in temperature – dry and rainy seasons more than hot or cold are the changes that people notice most.

Microclimates

Factors that modify these global climates at a local scale are topography, shelter and altitude. These create microclimates, very localised climates that differ from the dominant regional weather. The microclimate is what we actually experience at the human or garden scale.

Altitude and topography have a very significant influence. High and exposed locations are colder and more prone to rain and winds. Shelter from surrounding buildings and tree cover are important too – they reduce wind speeds and help maintain a warmer temperature.

Proximity to large water bodies, especially the sea, also impacts. These large water bodies hold significant heat energy that is stored through summer and slowly radiated back through winter, warming the air that passes over it. Hence many coastal areas can grow less hardy plants that will not survive inland.

Big variations in topography, especially in mountain ranges, also affect rainfall and divert winds. Moist air is drawn by winds towards the top of the mountains, where the moisture precipitates before it crosses the top. The air, without much moisture left, crosses the mountains and creates a drier leeward side, called the 'rain shadow'. The mountains act as reservoirs for the precipitation, especially where there are forests that slow runoff and where altitude and temperature allow snow to settle that stores the water until snowmelt.

Such a combination of dry (and often cloud free) land downwind of mountains, with large water reserves available nearby, creates the ideal conditions for some of the most important food producing landscapes globally – the Sierra Nevada ranges of Southern Spain and California are examples.

Shelter is another important factor that determines microclimate, usually caused by a barrier that stops or slows winds and blocks precipitation. Barriers may be solid structures, such as walls, that block or slow wind speed by friction. However, solid walls can actually create turbulence that may cause more eddies and gusting than if the wall was not there. In gardens, an ideal windbreak, therefore, is not a solid barrier, better is a screen that is partly permeable to slow the wind rather than completely block it. Most effective is a fence or barrier with 50-60% porosity, such as woven hurdles of Willow or Hazel, living hedges or rows of trees.

Shelter is not just good for our comfort, it helps pollinators to fly on days that would otherwise be too difficult for them. It also helps the earliest spring flowers and autumn flowers survive storm and frost – the flowers that are so important for sustaining biodiversity either side of the summer bounty.

Heat islands

Towns and cities are warmer than the surrounding land. This is known as the urban heat island effect and it happens for several reasons. First, rainfall runs quickly off hard surfaces into drains rather than evaporating (evaporating water takes heat and cools its surroundings). Lower cover of vegetation than in the countryside also limits evaporation. Secondly, the large surface area of stone and tarmac absorbs summer heat and radiates it back. Thirdly, factories, cars and houses produce 'waste heat'. Finally, tall buildings can create 'urban canyons' that obstruct air movement and further reduce cooling.

Together these mean that cities can be up to 7 degrees warmer than surrounding land. As with coastal areas, this makes it possible for a wider range of species to survive the winter. In our gardens, plants and overwintering animals that are sheltered by hedges or trees and live near walls, also experience warmer microclimates. Walls have two beneficial effects for them – wind speed is reduced, and heat is stored. This is, of course, why walled gardens were used to grow newly introduced tender plants before heated greenhouse technology developed. Heligan gardens in Cornwall demonstrates this technology.

Plants and climate

Plants come to our gardens from hugely different climates across the world, how do they cope with the change? Fortunately, plant life has the ability to tolerate large environmental variations. That plants can adjust when travelling from Earth to space without gravity, is a clear illustration that life has great adaptability built in. Coping with relatively small climate shifts sits well within many plants' capabilities.

Animals have another option if conditions really do not suit them – they can creep indoors with us. Many invertebrates do this, especially spiders and some butterflies, but you may find others, even slugs and snails may take the chance to creep inside.

This ability to adjust to change is an important survival

mechanism, essential for an unpredictable world. That does not mean, of course, that climate change is not a threat. Unfortunately there will be many losses, but thankfully we can hold on to some hope. After millions of years of evolution and survival, life has proven its resilience. Many plants and animals will survive the changes to come, take refuge, migrate or evolve to continue world-making.

Chapter 6

The Earth Below

Having looked at one vast ecosystem, the air above, I would like to now look down at another – the underground world that, like the air, is key to our survival.

Soils are not only important habitats in their own right, they also sustain and make possible every living thing on the surface. Soil ecosystems are as rich and as complex as any rainforest or coral reef – just darker and smaller and therefore harder to see. In this chapter we will look at what the soils do and how they do it. Do not underestimate them. Soils may have made life possible and soils preserve us.

Soil life, what lives beneath our feet

We are encouraged by TV documentaries to think of wilderness as sweeping landscapes populated by large and charismatic wild creatures, but why should that be? As Wendell Berry says, beneath the ground is also a teeming wilderness. In this soil wilderness, bacteria and other wild creatures are carrying on the fundamental work of decomposition, humus making, water storage, and flood control. Thoreau said, "wildness is the preservation of the world". He may have meant this as a philosophical or even spiritual concept, but when it comes to soils it is a hard fact.

What is soil?

A friend of mine who is a building engineer refers to any soil as mud. For most of us it is a mystery. I would like to take a moment here to explore in outline at least – what is soil, anyway? Where does it come from?

Soil is a mix of minerals, organic matter (dead or alive), air and water. Together these form an intricate structure of pores, channels and clumps. Soil is a finely balanced living system that holds air, water and nutrients, and sustains roots, micro-organisms and all of the life that lives beneath our feet. Soils are as diverse as any complex ecosystem, like the rainforests or the oceans, both in their makeup and the communities they support.

Soil minerals

The inorganic minerals in soil come from millennia of breakdown of underlying bedrock by weather, glaciers, roots and lichens. A healthy soil needs the right blend of mineral particles of different sizes, as together these form a matrix for the living community to inhabit. By convention, these different-sized particles are classified into groups, determined by size and behaviour.

Clays are the smallest particles less than 0.02mm in size.
Silt is 0.02mm to 0.5mm.
Sand is the term for particles of 0.5mm to 2mm diameter.
Stones and gravels are the largest 2mm to 15mm and above.

The wonder of clays

Clays are the very tiniest of the soil particles. All particle sizes are useful in building healthy productive soils but clays have unique properties, without which our gardens and farms, or we ourselves, would likely not survive. Clays are amongst the most amazing and most important mineral structures on Earth. If they were alive, they would be voted top like the bees.

We know something of their function in keeping soils productive, but they are still revealing their full story to us. Not only are clays small, they have complex and intricate fractal structures that have only been visible to us since electron microscopes were invented, which is why we are still learning about them. Now we can see in detail what forms they take, we learn that some look like crystal grottoes, some like fairy castles, some like mosses, some like lungs, trees or estuaries – they are the closest that the mineral world comes to living form.

Because they have a relatively large surface area for their size, clays have many important properties. They hold onto soluble nutrients and water that would otherwise drain away to rivers and the sea. Clays keep these resources safe for tiny roots to use. Clays have electric charges at their edges that hold onto things, or onto each other. They are also, therefore, the glues that allow bigger lumps to form with the sands and stones, and hold together to make the crucial soil matrix. Too little clay and everything will crumble apart and wash away.

The sheltering power of clay may even have paid a vital role in helping life to evolve on Earth. The first organic molecules are believed to have formed in the sea where there are lots of chemicals, but no boundaries. Long before life got close to developing its own protective skins or shells, it somehow organised into functioning systems and was able to shelter from storms, volcanic eruptions and damaging radiation. It is believed that this early critical shelter may have come from the clays.

In simulated ancient seawater, clay forms a hydrogel – a mass of microscopic spaces capable of holding liquids like a sponge. It has been suggested that over billions of years, chemicals sheltered in those spaces could have carried out the complex reactions that formed proteins, DNA and eventually all the machinery that makes a living cell work. Clay hydrogels could have protected those chemical processes until the membranes that surround the living cells developed.

Be thankful for the gift of clays, without them we possibly would not be here.

Importance of sands and silts

While clay plays a crucial role, too much of it is not a good thing. In mass, clay creates a sticky heavy soil that is too easy to compress into a solid mass that impedes air, holds too much water and can make it hard for plant roots to thrive. Clay needs help to make a productive soil and this comes from silts and sands and organic matter.

Silt is the name for particles of 0.002mm to 0.05mm. It is the inbetweenie of soil particles, neither as active or as binding as clay, nor as inert as sand. Silts are also very fine particles that can make fertile soils in their own right. Silt soils can grow many things, but they can be dusty and prone to erosion. Silts are frequently swept up by rivers and deposited again in large areas in places that were once wetlands, thereby making soils that are dominated by silt. Silt soils are common in East Anglia and the Netherlands.

Sand is the term for mineral particles of 0.5mm to 2mm diameter. Sands are not reactive and hold no nutrients or moisture, though there may be a thin film of water that surrounds each particle. Sands are the moderators of the soil, they leaven a mix that would otherwise be too sticky and airless. Sands on mass, without other materials, form inert, drought-prone, nutrient-poor soils that only a few specialised plants can thrive in.

Stones and gravels are the largest particles, from 2mm up to the size of boulders. Stones buried in soil are mostly just inert lumps, contributing little beyond drainage and keeping air channels open. Mostly they are waiting to be broken down into more useful sizes. On the surface of the soil, however, it is a different story. Stones in the garden are like oases in the desert and there will always be something attracted there. Humid, sheltered and safe from attack, life beneath a stone suits many small creatures, especially in extreme weather. It is a good idea to keep a stone pile in the garden as a refuge for wildlife; many creatures will gather there, breed, nest and survive the winter.

Soil texture – how to name and identify soils

Soil texture is a classification system that describes soil character and behaviour based on the proportions of sand, clay and silt. There are several different texture categories depending on the mix: as shown in this diagram known as the soil texture triangle.

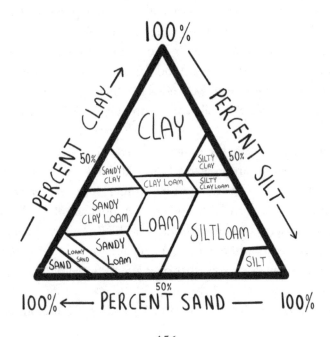

By identifying which texture we have in our gardens, we can predict how the soil will behave and how well it will grow the plants we need it to.

Loams, the centrists

In the middle of the triangle you will see there is a group of soils known as loams. Many people will have heard the term loam without realising it has a precise definition. Loams are the soils with the most even and balanced proportions of each particle size. They are regarded as the most productive and easiest soils to manage. Every gardener's guide ever written will tell you that plants 'prefer' a well-drained fertile loam in sun or partial shade – no surprises, it's like saying fish 'prefer' water to bonfires and it is, in fact, a huge simplification.

Loams certainly are the easiest, most reliable soils; they do suit most plants and offend few. They are the 'beige' of soils, the centrist soils. Yet, as we have seen, many plants have specialised adaptations – some prefer cliffs, some love chalk, others stone walls or concrete posts. Every environment has species that belong there and are adapted to that life.

Don't let the ideal of a perfect loam blind you to the qualities of other soil types, even those that are not recognisable as soil at all. There will be wonders growing in unlikely places, from those on your rooftops through to those thriving in the hostile desert of your bonfire ash.

From looking at the chart, you notice that adding clays to sands can bring them closer to loams in their behaviour. This is a practice that farmers sometimes do. They call it marling as marl – a lime-rich well-structured clay – is often used. Conversely, the amount of sand needed to add to clays to change them to loams is so huge that this option is impractical.

Soil structure

Soil particles usually bind together into large clods – the scientific name for these is peds. Between these clods are the essential large pores where most soil water drainage occurs and air enters the soil. Soil structure is the term given to the pattern of clods and channels. The structure is determined by the texture as modified by weather, animals and roots that create the channels and mix in the organic matter. Soils rich in clay and organic matter will form clods more easily than sandy and silty soils that tend to remain a looser mass of particles. The channels allow larger plant roots to reach depth and even within the clods there will be many microscopic channels where air and water is stored, accessible only to the smallest and finest plant roots.

Losing structure

Clay loams are the most fertile and productive soils as long as they retain a structure with sufficient air and drainage channels. If clay soils are put under heavy pressure, especially when wet, the structure can be destroyed and the channels lost. This is unfortunately common when builders are driving heavy machinery repeatedly across a soil, and in new houses you may find you inherit a soil that is compacted and airless – closer to a potter's clay than a healthy ecosystem. At this point you will be especially thankful that every plant does not really need a well-drained loam.

The best way to improve compacted heavy clay soils is by digging in lots of fine organic matter and adding gypsum which provides calcium in a soluble form. The gypsum reacts chemically with charges on the clay particles and makes them less sticky.

Organic matters

Soils are not just a mineral matrix. They also need an organic component, and this is made up of a mix of dead and living things, their wastes, and partially decomposed humus and organic matter.

Organic matter is the collective name given to the decomposed remains of once-living things in the soil – roots no longer needed, fungi and micro-organisms that have lived their lives, remains of leaves, dropped banana skins and your long-gone pet hamster, and all of our ancestors too – all the way back to the very first living things that built their bodies out of air, sunlight and water. In his 2018 book, *Caesar's Last Breath*, Sam Kean argues that in our lifetime we will breathe in many air molecules breathed out by Caesar as he lay dying. His point is that the elements of the world do not disappear, but are endlessly and efficiently recycled. The same is true of soils. Maybe at some time in our lives we walk over molecules of Caesar himself, returned to the air after burial, recaptured by trees and given to your garden soil. What a journey he had.

Recycling is an important part of what soil does for us. Over time, organic remains are digested by micro-organisms and broken down into their constituent molecules that are released back into the world to be used again. Soils are the world's recycling factories, clays and humus are the factory floors where this work gets done.

Humus

Gardeners of a certain generation will know that 'humus' was a favourite topic for David Bellamy. Even so, we can be confident that few of us really understand what humus really is. We know this because even the world's leading soil scientists confess that they are only just beginning to unravel what humus is and how it works.

As dead organic matter is digested by micro-organisms, most of it returns to the air as carbon dioxide and water vapour, and minerals that cannot turn to gasses remain in the soil. Finally, as all of the easily recyclable elements are released and re-used, we are left with a dark, sweet smelling spongy material with an intricate fractal structure. This is humus.

Humus is carbon in such a tough molecular form, that when sheltered in the soil it can resist further decay for hundreds of years. Humus is such a complex substance that it has been described as 'molecules of radical disarray' or as a biological 'performance' rather than matter. The meaning is that, despite its minute size, it is very active and does a lot.

Like clays, the spongy structure of humus holds onto nutrients and water and stops them draining to the sea before they can be used again. Humus and clay together ensure that nutrients only pass to plants on demand rather than as a fast food rush, as comes from artificial fertilisers. Humus also holds the most water of any soil component. Soils rich in humus are fertile and stay moist even in drought. Humus also puts coats on clays, stopping everything getting too sticky.

Although humus is tough and potentially long-lasting, it will break down when broken up and exposed to air. It takes time but eventually bacteria will eat it. Have you ever kept a pot plant on the windowsill for years and then one day you look inside to find the roots spiralling in apparent emptiness – the compost seems to have evaporated? That, in fact, is exactly what has happened. Thanks to microbes, the compost has rejoined the air as carbon dioxide.

Soil layers – the horizons

Soil is usually made up of different layers, with distinct properties at different depths. These are referred to as soil horizons.

Topsoil

Topsoil is the uppermost layer, richest in organic matter, living and dead, and with more air than lower down. This is where most humus is found, the most available water and most nutrients, most plant roots too. The topsoil is the most fertile layer that our food production relies on. It is also where the seed bank shelters.

Subsoil

Beneath the topsoil is the subsoil, with less roots, less life and less organic matter. The subsoil is mainly derived from the underlying bedrock and is mostly inert inorganic material that has just begun its transformation into the complex mix that is true soil. Although less active or complex than topsoil – definitely matter rather than performance – subsoil is still important for plants, especially trees. It holds the biggest reservoir of water, accessed by the deepest roots. The open rocky nature of most subsoils allows excess water to drain to the underground aquifer or to nearby rivers. If this drainage doesn't happen, water stagnates in the surface soil layers, causing root death and maybe flooding.

Soil life

The next important organic component is living, the life that lives beneath us. Soils are home to many important and fascinating organisms, a soil is not a true soil without them.

The mites

Mites are tiny beneficial arthropods related to ticks and spiders. They are useful members of the Earth's recycling system and help to breakdown dead organic matter such as leaf litter, fungi, algae, and other natural debris. There are about twenty thousand different types of soil mites identified, and it is believed that about eighty thousand different types exist. This is again where we reach the boundaries of our current knowledge. It is highly likely that there are thousands of unknown mite species waiting undiscovered. We do know that the mites have diversified and have many different lifestyles. Some of them are very tiny predators which eat other soil-dwelling creatures such as bacteria and nematodes.

After it rains and the sun comes out you may spot tiny red specks walking on the surface of your garden path. These are probably Red Velvet mites, related to spiders and named after a cake, they live a life that feels like a studio Ghibli movie. When it is breeding season the male seduces the female by dancing, if he woos her they retreat to a love garden he built earlier from minute twigs. Despite its tiny size and loving nature, the Velvet mite can attack much larger creatures and helps to control plant pests.

Nematode worms – the majority?
Nematode worms are important and numerous in the garden soil community. They are so numerous that it has been estimated that an amazing 80% of animals on earth are nematodes (the rest of us are bit players apparently). Remember that bacteria are probably the real majority of all living things, but they are not classed as animals.

Nematodes, also known as roundworms or eelworms, are not closely related to earthworms. They feed on bacteria and plant roots. Humans rarely care about nematodes, except for the few that are pests that infect our pets or attack living plant roots. We put these with the squirrels on the naughty list. However, nematodes are not all bad, they are important members of the recycling teams. In turn, they are eaten by mites and fungi, so they support the food chain. Given that they are so numerous, they provide lots of food for others.

It has been calculated that there is up to 60 billion nematodes for every human on the planet. Nobody knows for sure how many species of nematode exist, but estimates are of a million species. They are found in every ecosystem, in the sea, even in deep trenches, in forests, the polar regions, deserts and even mountain tops. Normally only a few millimetres long, the largest nematode found was nearly 2m in size. It lived so deep underground no one suspected it was there. Doubtless many more wonders are lying beneath our feet awaiting future discovery, and probably hoping we don't find them.

Earthworms

Earthworms, in contrast, are much better understood and loved – like the bees, we know that we need them. Earthworms are well adapted to living underground where they breathe through their permeable skin. They live by burrowing through the soil, ingesting it as they go. They feed on organic content and excrete the remainder as worm casts.

Worldwide there are over 3,000 species of earthworm identified so far. 27 species live in the UK. Although they can hold their breath for several days if they have to, earthworms don't generally like waterlogged soils. After rain they often come to the surface where you will see birds feeding on them.

The different species of earthworm have diverse lifestyles. Some live in compost, some in permanent burrows deep down in the soil, while others are content with higher ground and make networks of tunnels just below the surface. Some are surface living and survive in a covering of dead leaves, grass or rotting vegetation.

There is still a lot we don't know about earthworms but we do know that they are invaluable for healthy soils and many species depend on them for food – our favourite songbirds and hedgehogs amongst them.

Along with plants, earthworms were a favourite subject of study for the young Charles Darwin who was fascinated by how they turned the soil and took dead leaves that fertilised the lower layers. He called them 'nature's plough'. In his eccentric early experimental style Darwin tested their behaviour. He offered them different types of food. He recorded that they preferred Wild Cherry and Carrots, raw fat to raw meat and that, 'judging by their eagerness for certain kinds of food, they must enjoy the pleasures of eating'.

He also tested their senses by exposing the worms to lamps or candlelight, and their sensitivity to temperature by holding 'a poker heated to dull redness near some worms'. Earthworms do not have ears, but Darwin still tried to test their hearing. He played a metal whistle and had his son play his bassoon loudly at them. Darwin even shouted at the worms, but found that they showed no response. However, he did establish that earthworms are extremely sensitive to vibration, and if placed on a piano they reacted to the sound.

Earthworms are vital to soil health because they transport nutrients and minerals from deeper to surface layers. They also take organic debris downwards. Also, the channels they dig are helpful for drainage and for air to reach plant roots.

As with many soil eating organisms, worms have evolved to cope with whatever they encounter. They have gut defences that allow them to ingest pollutants which they can convert to a less toxic form. They are so effective at soil formation in difficult conditions, that researchers are studying how they cope with simulated Martian soils. Like the Tardigrades, it looks like earthworms may also join the space race.

From sea to land

Now we turn to another group of soil dwellers – the molluscs and crustaceans. These remind us of how animal life first crawled from the sea and now live underground with the fossils of their distant ancestors.

Crustaceans

Crustaceans are also arthropods. It is a classification that includes crabs, lobsters and giant clams. Recently there have been trials in using insects as food – be careful if you are allergic to shellfish as their close relationship means they could cause a similar reaction.

Across much of the world, land crabs and the smaller sand hoppers are the most common crustaceans that join us on shore. We also have one much smaller land crustacean in the garden – these are the Woodlice or Pill Bugs. There are 35 species of woodlouse in the UK, five of which are common. It has been said that their common names are countless and much more diverse than the creatures themselves, probably reflecting their fascination to children. Slaters and Wood Pigs were the names used in my childhood, the ones that curl in balls are often called Pill Bugs.

Woodlice reveal their marine evolution by the fact that they breathe through gills. On land, they survive only in dark damp places, feeding off rotting wood and decaying vegetation, so they are also part of the essential recycling squads.

Molluscs

Another group that bridges land and sea are the molluscs. There are many thousands of mollusc species in the world and they encompass most that we know as seafood other than fish. Many have shells like clams and oysters, some live without, like squid and octopus.

A subdivision of molluscs that live on land are the gastropods and these are our garden nemesis – slugs and snails. Both are, as we know, voracious plant eaters, although their primary role is recycling rotting organic matter. Research shows that on average only 10% of their daily diet is plants that we cherish. Slugs have even been known to tackle dog excrement on the ground, not hanging from a tree.

For some reason, young Darwin seems to have been uninterested in this group, or today we would know much more, including whether bassoon playing, metal whistles, blindfolds, hot pokers or pianos are deterrents. I suspect many gardeners already know that shouting does not bother them. Without Darwin's help, gardeners resort to a weird and wonderful range of slug control techniques.

One is the barrier idea – putting protective defences around tender seedlings. Salt does work but only when it is dry enough to not wash away. My own experience is that, given that most slugs shelter underground, barriers give only limited protection. They are more effective against larger snails who, with their shells, cannot burrow. I have found that fire ash in a thick layer, or rosemary or conifer twigs, can have some success too. Dried seaweed is even better as it contains salt, which they hate. In the modern age we can go high tech with copper strips or even electric fences but I have never found these better than ash or seaweed. Beer traps are effective if rather harrowing as the slugs drown in a disgusting beer/slug soup. Whoever thought of this method I wonder? I can't think of any other pest where our approach to control is to get them so smashed that they drown and dissolve in their own temptation.

Some bad news is that the technique of lobbing them over the fence is futile because snails and slugs have a homing instinct. Unless you get them at least 20 metres away they will find their way back. The other thing that defeats us, is their phenomenal reproductive rate. It has been calculated that the number of slugs in the average garden is equivalent to two large fully grown rabbits grazing all of the time. In research it was found that, dishearteningly, removing 10–20,000 slugs a year from a garden over 4 years did not change the active population longer term. To a degree it does help if we can limit their breeding spaces. Despite the general value of leaf litter in the garden, it is probably a good idea not to let too much rotting vegetation gather at the base of prized plants that you want to protect.

Until recently the salvation for most gardeners was that nature knows how to maintain a balance. The best defences against slug attacks are usually the ones that plants have for themselves, and there is a wide range of plants that for whatever reason, the slugs simply do not touch. Obviously they find it difficult to eat woody shrubs like Roses, Cistus, Lavender or Rosemary, leaving these to the muntjacs or wallabies. Even among the softer herbaceous plants many are unassailable – the Geranium family seem to be completely shunned, even the seedlings of the fragile looking Herb Robert. Slugs also make no dents in Euphorbias, Ferns or Japanese Anemones. On the other hand, if you are determined to grow Hostas or Dahlias you may as well put up a sign saying 'free lunch' and in wetter places like Cornwall they can be tatters within hours of planting.

In commercial horticulture, especially where there are safety concerns for staff and public, a trend to avoid chemicals is now the norm. During my career I have lost count of the chemicals, especially herbicides, that I was told were harmless and since proved otherwise. Therefore, I will always forsake chemicals in favour of smarter solutions, for example using mulches to reduce weeds and biological controls for pests. Recently there has been an introduction that could prove to be a boon for gardeners – nematodes that control slugs.

Soil bacteria

Amongst the many members of the soil community, bacteria have the greatest number and the greatest biomass. It is believed that up to 10 billion bacteria live in each gram of soil – 10 billion lives, 10 billion creative beings. We have known for centuries of the soil wilderness near the surface – the jungles of worms, roots, beetles, ants and fungi. Yet the latest scientific research is revealing a vast new ecosystem deeper below that we had not suspected. This is termed the deep biosphere.

A vast new undiscovered ecosystem

It has been found that 70% of the bacteria on earth is living deep underground, containing collectively over 20 billion tons of carbon. This is more than the entire mass of humans above ground. This deep biosphere begins a few metres down and extends as deep as five kilometres.

Each of these deep bacterial lives may perform feats of chemical ingenuity, most of which have never been studied. Who knows what marvels these creatures will reveal to us in the coming centuries? This ecosystem is essential to life on the surface and we are only just beginning to explore it.

The soil food chain

Who is the top predator in the soil jungle? Gradually the things that feed on other things get bigger. As we climb the pyramid of soil life, we reach the insects and the earthworms; these in turn feed mammals such as moles and hedgehogs, and, of course, the songbirds, in a strict pecking order every morning. Although they do not live underground, songbirds like Robins are so dependent on the soil that they could be reasonably called part of the soil community. As can humans? The difference is that the Robins possibly know it, while humans seem largely unaware.

Our gardens, and indeed the entire Earth, are positioned between two vast and rich ecosystems that sustain us – earth and air. In order to function properly, they must exchange and communicate – these two great ecosystems need connectors. There are certain agents that link the above and below ground worlds, and carry things between them, as emissaries or disrupters – these are also key workers:

Rain and lightning return dusts, sulphur and nitrogen, from the air to the soil.

Bacteria move nitrogen and sulphur from the air to the earth below.

Plants, with the help of worms and other soil creatures, move carbon from the air to the earth below, and they move soil minerals from the earth to our bodies. Later these minerals travel back to the soil or the air, depending on how the recycling creatures treat our remains.

Mankind, fungi and other animal life, especially the recycling creatures, balance the flow. Along with fires and volcanoes their role is to take from the earth and return to the air – carbon, sulphur, nitrogen, minerals and dusts, where they cycle again.

h

Chapter 7

Changes – The Daily Cycle and the Garden Year

We have looked at the cast of creatures and the two vast stage sets, the twin ecosystems of the earth and the air.

Our next consideration is what plays out on these stages – next I want to look at the cycles and changes that make up the unfolding garden year.

Like us, and the creatures that live there, the garden itself has a circadian rhythm – a daily cycle that keeps everything healthy and gives insights into how the world keeps a balance.

The day unfolding

Everything you see happening in the garden happens for a reason, reflecting problems solved by millions of years of evolution. One common problem that all life faces is how to share resources and get to them safely, a problem we ourselves have been reminded of by Covid-19. Birds and insects solve this problem by timing their flights to when there are fewer potential dangers and when food is readily available. Flowers also adjust their behaviour to suit their pollinators and ensure safe feeding.

Evidence of this is that different flowers have evolved different times to open. This was first shown in 1745 when Carl van Linnaeus made the world's first flower clock in Uppsala, Sweden. He planted a bed with patches of different flowers, by which he was able to tell the time of day. Here are the patterns of flower opening he observed:

5:00 am: Poppy
6:00 am: Bindweed
7:00 am: Coltsfoot, Dandelion
8:00 am: Cowslip
10:00 am: Sorrel
11:00 am: Common Sow-thistle
12:00 pm: Ice plant
4:00 pm: Marvel of Peru
8:00 pm: Evening Primrose

As evening approaches, the flowers that are moth pollinated begin to open and the bee pollinated flowers start to close. Job done for the day, they tuck themselves up for their night of rest. Starting when the sun warms the air enough, you will also see shifts of workers and feeders join the flowers. The pollinators come in waves too, each heading for the flower it likes best as they open in anticipation.

The yearly cycles

Moving on from the daily pattern, let us focus now on yearly cycles and how our natural neighbours come and go and how they change their behaviour in sequence with the changing seasons.

Whether they are permanent garden residents, or travellers, bird behaviour changes so dramatically with the seasons that they, with the plants, provide us with the most obvious markers of the turning of the year.

Even as early as the winter solstice, marginally lengthening days and occasional mild weather spells can trigger breeding preparations in birds. Their main response is increasing amounts of song and the first duets are heard. That this can happen even while they are still scraping for food and trying to survive the long cold nights seems remarkable. Despite the weather, hormones are rising. The birds must sing now and make the first scouts for nest material.

The next generation

By February, breeding preparations are fully underway. Singing and displaying are important activities so that birds either find a new mate or revive an existing attachment. February can be harder on the birds than January – the weather is still harsh, last year's nuts and fruits are long gone and insects are only just emerging. This hardship inevitably costs lives and territories and relationships change.

Normally birds time their breeding to the warmest part of the year, when there is plenty of food and lots of daylight in which to find it. However, with the trend for less harsh winters, breeding attempts are starting earlier, especially amongst those birds with access to feeders and therefore with the time and resources to breed earlier. However, for most birds, early broods rarely survive. Exceptions are Pigeons and Doves that are typically midwinter breeders.

From March to July, breeding hits its peak and songs fill the air. The first songsters of the season are winter residents such as Robins and Great Tits, joined later by migrants like Chiffchaffs and Blackcaps, to make May and June the peak time for the dawn chorus.

Songs are key in mate selection and researchers believe that the mental agility required to learn songs are signs of fitness that a female will use for mate selection. Songs trigger the initial interest and first contact, but a courtship is required to confirm a bond. During the courtship the male and female synchronise their sexual readiness.

Their next major task is to find and secure territory for feeding and raising the chicks. Territory secured, nest building is the next occupation, and through March birds will be seen busily gathering materials.

Songs also help males secure their patch from competitors. Songs are threats against encroachment, they enable the birds to determine their hierarchies without physical confrontation. To both other males and females a song is a revealing disclosure of the singer. For birds, communication by song is rich with meaning, much like scent communication between other animals.

Songs can reveal age, health, vigour, intelligence and status. No matter how similar they sound to us, every song is different and birds pick up every nuance.

The great arrival

Birders call it the great arrival. Every spring some 6-10 million birds arrive in Britain from distant forests and deserts to make their summer homes, and in doing so they make our gardens more colourful and musical. From March onwards the diversity of birds in the garden changes. Chiffchaffs are often the first arrivals, best identified by the song that echoes its name – chiff, chaff, chiff, chaff.

How do millions of birds creep up on us? Because they come in small groups and travel mostly at night, we do often miss that we are gifted with one of the planet's greatest wonders of migration. We wake up in the morning and there they are – like all good magic is supposed to work.

The birds have been making these journeys for tens of thousands of years. Changing climate is beginning to affect the timing of bird migrations but so far not more than they can adapt to. By May and June the air hunters arrive; Swifts, Swallows, Martins, Flycatchers and Warblers. Their timing coincides with peaks of insect activity as, in the daytime cycle, food and feeder are synchronised in their monthly patterns.

New year, new clothes

After the breeding season, the birds have another preoccupation. At least once a year, the birds moult – they lose their old feathers and regrow new ones. Feathers wear out as the year progresses. Flying, rubbing against neighbouring feathers or trees, general weakening due to exposure to sun, along with the impact of parasites such as feather lice, all cause damage.

By moulting, shedding and regrowing these feathers, they shed parasites as well. Adult birds replace their worn-out feathers from the year's season and grow new, strong, warm feathers to see them through the winter. This year's young are losing their first feathers and growing their first adult coats.

Like our hair, feathers grow from follicles in the skin and the growth of a new feather from the bottom pushes the old one out. The process occurs in sequence across the skin to ensure that there are no 'bald' patches. This means that a full moult may spread out over a long time, which is fine if there is a plentiful food supply, and if the bird is not a migrant facing a long urgent journey. Moulting is a risky time, however. It drains a bird's resources. It takes energy to grow new feathers – there could be heat loss when feathers are shed, and when flight feathers are lost, more energy may be needed for flight. This is why many birds become inconspicuous for a time in summer and there is less song. They are more vulnerable to predation during moulting time. Generally, moults do not overlap with other demands on a bird's energy, such as breeding or migration. Moulting patterns depend upon species, a bird's age and the time of year.

By September, all moulting is finished, new feathers are in place and the residents appear in fresh attire. By now the gardens are still quieter. Many singers are off travelling and for those remaining, the need to declare and defend breeding territories is over.

Finding food for lockdown

Although insect biomass increases with warm weather, not everything goes smoothly, even in summer. Dry weather can make life difficult for the ground feeders, as foraging becomes harder work and earthworms and other ground insects all dig deeper into the earth.

By August, a hint of autumn is already in the air. The birds know it and in their own way they make preparations for what is coming. Migrants preparing to fly back to their winter refuges have to feed and build their energy.

Those who remain as residents have to feed too, instead of a journey they have a winter to endure. Fortunately, in the garden, fruits, nuts and seeds reach their full abundance. In this run up to winter or migration, even previously insectivorous birds will include fruits and nuts in their diets.

One by one, the migrant visitors leave the mix. Most sorely missed are the screaming aerial ballets of the Swifts; the air is suddenly empty of aerobatics. Sparrows, too, may seem less active at the feeders. They will not have gone far but they do take trips to nearby countryside to find their favourite foods at this time – grains, hedgerow berries and insects. After harvest in September, they usually return to their home garden and become your neighbours again, rejoining the birds that are resolutely holding their patch through winter. These are the Tits, Robins, Wrens and Blackbirds mostly, the birds that are used to finding shelter as cold settles in. This is when nest boxes and tree cavities become most treasured.

Robins are an exception, noted for their persistence at singing through darkness – during dark winter days and even sometimes at night. They are again singing to defend territory, but now it is a feeding territory not a breeding territory – the patch that will, hopefully, see them through the winter. With survival at stake, this is when the Robin gets its reputation for aggression and scuffles between birds are common. It is time for puffed up red breasts, and finally, if all else fails, a fight must follow.

October is often when birds start flocking together, usually a single species or sometimes as mixed gatherings. The flocks are for mutual protection and for sharing learning. October is when many birds go back to college.

Others, like the Jays, are spending this time foraging and storing food. Jays love gathering acorns and finding safe places to store them. It is not just the Jays that do this, Nuthatches and Coal Tits will also take food off to a store. This is another demonstration of birds' mental ability – they must not only identify and remember good trees to collect from, they must identify safe hiding places and keep them in their long term memory. Even so, not every acorn stored is retrieved and eaten, some survive and germinate. Jays help oaks to move and reforest the landscape by transporting seed that is too heavy to travel by its own means.

Sowing the seed

Berrying plants also use birds to carry their seeds to new places. This is another important and ancient plant and animal partnership. It seems that, unlike with insects and flowers, scent plays little role in attracting birds to berries. Birds are well adapted to spotting their food, they have good colour vision and can identify berries from a distance. As with flowers and pollinators, the match is well evolved. Plants grow fruits that are perfectly synched with the vision of birds. Blue, black or purple berries sometimes reflect UV light that the birds see better than we do.

Preferred fruit is influenced by the size of bird. Blackbirds will eat almost any berry, including Sloes and Rosehips, while smaller birds prefer small berries, like Cotoneaster and Hawthorn. The birds of woodland floors, like Robins, tend to rely on insects in the undergrowth, and berries like Elder and Ivy that are found close to their normal habitats.

Finding shelter

As winter approaches, with larders stocked and fat laid down, the remaining urgent task is to find shelter for winter. The thick dense cover of hedges gives many birds life-saving protection, as does the dense evergreen foliage of conifers. Climbing plants against walls or tree trunks also provide essential warmth and dryness through winter storms. Both are useful features to add to your gardens, as are the berrying and winter flowering plants we have already talked about.

Invertebrates also face the winter with a range of techniques for surviving. After a summer spent feeding, pollinating, and mating, in the autumn they too begin preparation for the ordeal to come. As cold-blooded creatures, the winter is their greatest challenge. They tackle it in three main ways:

Many overwinter in dormant forms as eggs or pupae sheltered in dead leaves, wood and stone piles, hollow standing vegetation, or crevices in old trees and walls.

Some hibernate as adults in the same warm, sheltered spots such as bird houses, natural hollows in trees, log piles, rock crevices and stone walls. Spiders and some butterflies may also spend the winter in a corner of your shed, garage or outhouse, anywhere they find a crack to get inside.

Of the 58 species of butterfly in Britain, 9 survive winter as an egg, 32 as a caterpillar, 11 as a pupa, and 6 as adults. About 5 are sunseekers, migrating to escape the winter as the birds do.

Moving in with us

Some invertebrates have learnt that the best shelter is inside a warm house and they have become our regular house companions through winter. From late August onwards, you may find your household is joined by the Giant House spider – welcomed as small friends, or feared, depending on your outlook. They are the largest spider of Northern Europe, the males with a leg span that can be up to 8cm across, and they are fast, capable of moving at half a metre per second. The females are much smaller and may live with you for several years. They spin sheet-like cobwebs in neglected corners such as behind the fireplace, or under the sofa, they also have a strange fondness for bathrooms where they wait to trap other house insects at night. The males have come inside in autumn for mating. Having paired and mated several times, the male dies and is eaten by the female.

More appealing to many people, the Small Tortoiseshell and Peacock butterflies often come indoors during early autumn when they are also looking for sheltered conditions to overwinter. It is actually best for them to shelter in a cool place like a shed or garage as they are prone to wake early in a warm house.

Another frequent visitor in late summer is that great favourite, the wasp! This is the time they become visible and persistent, searching for the sweetness they crave. Prior to this the female workers would have been focused on feeding their nests with protein-rich food. It is only when the workers leave the dying nests that they become sugar-hunters.

Awakenings

The timing of insect emergence from winter dormancy is very important. When they wake and get back outside from their nest or from your bathroom, they will urgently need access to the right food. The pollinators and flower feeders, like butterflies, must wait until the plants are out of hibernation too.

To better understand these seasonal patterns, remember that, with many arthropods, the larvae does all the feeding necessary to sustain them for weeks and months of their adult life. Adults can be short-lived, needing only quick fuel top-ups, usually nectar, or they may not even feed at all.

In spring and early summer, after mating, females lay their eggs. After just a week or two the larvae hatch and begin to feed, until it is time to undergo a transformation.

Time for new beginnings

Early summer is the time for changes and new beginnings. In Ireland, with characteristic poetry, they called lockdown for the very vulnerable 'cocooning'. This is an echo of one of the greatest miracles we see at this time of year, when caterpillars and many other insect larvae form cocoons and start a great transformation. Cocoons provide a protective coat for the extraordinary change into adulthood. The adults emerge in spring and summer to mate and breed, and begin the cycle again.

Extraordinary survivals

As well as their different techniques for living through adversity, arthropods also show a wide range of ways of escaping risks, such as long journeys to safe places. Appreciating the yearly migrations that happen around the world helps us understand why some species seem to arrive from nowhere and then disappear again. It also helps us understand how movement is an essential strategy for life. Later we will return to consider how these different survival strategies, honed over millions of years, can give us hope for the future.

Bird migrations are probably more familiar, but they are not the only creatures that undertake great journeys. There are many migratory insects too, including moths, dragonflies, ladybirds, hoverflies and even aphids. Climate change will bring more. Because insect migrations happen in dribs and drabs, or at heights we cannot see, we often have no idea of the scale of what is happening. Researchers have found each summer there may be movement of 3,200 tonnes of migrating insects from Britain to Africa. 3.5 trillion insects travel at heights of up to 1000m. There can be around four billion hoverflies alone that come each spring and go again each autumn.

These long-distance migrations don't just benefit the insects, but with them they bring pollen from distant plant populations to mix with our local ones. By introducing different climate adaptations into the gene pool, these insects may help prepare our wildflowers for a changing climate.

Butterfly journeys

It may seem hard to believe that the fragile wings of butterflies are powerful enough to fly for thousands of miles, but they manage it. Like mosses, they are not as fragile as they appear.

Unless they migrate, butterflies take refuge and overwinter as eggs, pupae or dormant adults. Winter fungal attack is a major cause of mortality, so they must stay cool and dry during the hibernating season. In any of these forms, most butterflies hibernate at least until the first warm days of spring, usually around the beginning of March.

As summer fades, the migratory butterflies leave for warmer places to overwinter. Amongst the UK butterflies, the Clouded Yellow, Large and Small Whites, Red Admiral and Painted Ladies are all migratory. The Red Admiral (*Vanessa atlanta*) fly to central and northern Europe every year from southern Europe or even North Africa. In autumn, their offspring migrate back southwards.

The Painted Lady is the UK's best-known migratory butterfly. It completes a 14,000 km round trip to sub-Saharan Africa for its winter period. Even this journey is not as impressive as the migrations of the Monarch butterfly in the USA. Monarch butterflies travel between 1,200 and 2,800 miles from the United States and Canada to central Mexico. There they hibernate in warm and humid mountain forests.

The ones that tough it out

Despite the storms and cold of winter, not all flying creatures choose dormancy or migration. A small group of hardy moths maintain adult activity in wintertime. These include the appropriately named, Winter moth, December moth and Spring Usher, so there is barely ever a time in the year when no pollinators at all are active. Fortunately for them there is barely ever a time in the year when no single flower is there to provide food.

Bees in winter

Bee behaviour in winter depends on where they normally live and whether they are solitary or colony bees. When it gets too cold to work and fly, honeybees huddle together in the hive to retain warmth. The primary aim is to keep the queen safe and warm and with this protection she may survive for 3-4 years. During this lockdown period, their honey stores provide a lifeline. However, since they are awake and need to void waste, they will go out and seek nectar on warmer winter days.

The various bumblebees have a different strategy. They have an annual life cycle. After the new queens are produced and mate in the summer and autumn, the workers, males and old queens die. By this time the females have probably left their eggs sealed inside a nest, in a cavity or burrow, provided with stores of pollen and nectar. They will have lined their nests with waterproof resin to protect their young from damp.

Solitary bees overwinter in different ways. Few solitary bees overwinter as adults. Except for Furrow bees, the adults usually die before winter comes. Furrow bees mate in the autumn after which the newly-mated queens may survive in hibernation through winter. Furrow bees are mining bees that burrow into soft earth and shelter under logs and stones to escape the frost. They prefer north-facing banks to avoid being warmed up too early by the winter sun. Some may still emerge confused on warm winter days. As we did ourselves in 2020 after weeks of cocooning.

Normally during the winter, sheltering and cocooning bees remain in a state of dormancy. They are ready to fly when the temperature rises, so they can take advantage of spring blossoms such as Willow, Blackthorn, Hawthorn and fruit trees. Those solitary bees that emerge in early spring, such as the early bumblebee, Tawny mining bees, Ashy mining bees and Red mason bees, grow from egg to adult over the summer. Ones that emerge in late spring or summer, such as Leafcutter bees, Wool Carder bees and Yellow-faced bees, grow from egg to larva over the summer, and overwinter in their larval stage. It may be too cold to feed and grow, even in their shelters, so these larvae survive in a state of torpor where they use little energy. They wait until spring before they pupate and turn into adults which fly out to feed on summer blooms.

These slightly different strategies ensure that we have a sequence of pollinators emerging as the flowers need them. It is also a way that they minimise the competition between them.

Helping them through the winter

The worrying decline in insect abundance is well documented. Accordingly we should use any opportunity to help them survive, especially through the cold and darkness. It is valuable, therefore, to plant winter flowers, such as Mahonia, Heathers, Winter Honeysuckle, Winter Aconite, Hellebores and Snowdrop. Also we should avoid disturbing their nesting places. Ideally avoid winter digging in areas where you have seen solitary bees. If you can't leave the soil alone, create other refuges, bee-friendly winter shelters for them somewhere out of the way. Make a log-pile, rockery or earth bank in a north-facing area of the garden. It also helps to leave old plant stems standing rather than clearing everything away. As well as solitary bees, these will be refuges for many overwintering insects.

First stirrings

As the hungry invertebrates emerge, hatch or migrate back each spring, their lives are synchronised with the growth of the plants that sustain them. January is changeover month for flowers, the last of the useful winter blooms are joined gradually by the earliest spring arrivals. Much, of course, depends on temperature and how hard the winter is, but in mild years the first Snowdrops could flower in January, along with Winter Aconite, *Eranthis hyemelis*, the first of the Buttercup family to appear each year.

In my garden it is usually Candlemas (around Feb 2nd), a date that coincides with the Celtic Fire Festival of Imbolc, that brings the first Crocus and Primrose flowers. Imbolc in Celtic tradition marks the end of winter and the first awakening of spring, an appropriate time for more flower colour to join us at last.

Daffodils and Narcissus are slower to appear. In fact I find that the variety of Daffodil 'February Gold' rarely gets out of bed before March. In contrast, in Cornwall and other mild spots, the variety 'Rijnveld's early sensation' can be in bloom before Christmas, often stoking concern about climate change, although this early rising is just its normal nature. By March, a wide variety of plants are in bloom including bulbs, Hellebores and the essential Pussy Willow that early insects love.

Frondescence

Frondescence is the word for the unfolding of leaves that had been packed tightly in buds. This too happens in sequence; bulbs, grasses and herbaceous plants come first, by May the trees and shrubs start to join them, and at this time there is so much frondescence you can almost hear it. This is a time of plenty for leaf-eating insects as well as pollinators – at last they can move from stored food to fresh salads. Caterpillars plump up ready to become summer wonders.

A change in the seasons

When we talk of the changing seasons, we cannot avoid the fact that they themselves are changing in unusual ways now; so here I would like to explore why we think of seasons in the way that we do, and also how these patterns we are so familiar with are changing. If climate change progresses as forecast, we must anticipate big shifts in familiar patterns.

Why do we see the seasons as we do?

How many seasons are there? Four, of course! Well, how do we know? Because we have been told so. In reality, this number of seasons is not a given and the yearly patterns are regarded differently across the world.

Even at home, through history the seasons have been seen quite differently to how we see them today. For much of UK history, the changing year was marked less by climate patterns than by key events in the agricultural cycle and by a procession of religious feasts and religious days. These sometimes had a link to climate but mostly they depended on cosmology and religious narrative to divide the year. The timing of these year markers was often determined by solar or lunar cycles rather than earthly changes. Only when printed calendars appeared, did it become possible to structure yearly events around a nominated date rather than natural phenomena.

An important question was who got to decide when these key dates were? Across Europe, since the Middle Ages, this remained in the control of powerful religious bodies, such as the Council of Tours. Pre-Christian times were different. In Europe and through much of our history, people had less scope (and less interest?) for structured and convoluted systems; it is believed that they tended to see the year as dominated by two obvious seasons – light and dark. This two-part division of the yearly cycle is often cited as being integral to Celtic seasonal lore. The dark half of the year was said to be when the evergreen Holly king ruled the winter forest and the Oak king retreated until summer returned.

The recognition and naming of spring and autumn as distinctive seasons is relatively recent in our culture, only becoming widely recognised around the 16th century. This change was linked especially to Renaissance interest in classical teachings. As with the classical elements, it was the ancient Greek philosophers, especially Aristotle, who defined the division of the year into four seasons, each running from solstice to equinox or equinox to solstice.

Thanks to the work of scholars like Francis Bacon, these ideas became accepted throughout Medieval Europe, as can be seen in many of Shakespeare's writings. The belief in humours survived until at least Elizabethan times, after which it was replaced by scientific frameworks. Even so, the idea of four seasons remains entrenched in our cultural understanding of how the earth cycles and how the year progresses.

Different perspectives on the seasons

Away from temperate climates and cultures, other societies saw things quite differently. Even today, the way that people see the seasons is as diverse as cultures and climates are. For people in the tropics the temperature is much less changeable through the year than in northern countries, and fluctuations in rainfall are more significant. As a result, their year is often divided into just two seasons, wet and dry, although this may be complemented by periods of dominant climatic events, such as 'hurricane season' or 'fire season'.

In some Asian philosophies and cosmologies, the idea of five elements was more typical. They, in turn, derived five seasons from this cosmology. In India, six seasons, linked to the religious calendar, is long established. Many indigenous communities in North America and Australia also see the year as divided into five or six, signalled by natural phenomena such as the timing of ice melting or animal migrations. In the floodplains of major rivers, it can be the changes in river behaviour – flood or low water – that most defines the seasonal calendar. This was true along the Nile in Ancient times.

What can we learn from this diversity?

Really the detail is not important. What is obvious is that the seasons as we describe them are a cultural construct not a fixed reality. The reality is that the year changes in a gradual cyclical way that can be divided and named however we wish. With this understanding, and particularly in times of changing climate, it may be useful to free ourselves from inherited dogma. We are free to look beyond what we have been told. We can become natural philosophers, observing and reflecting about the reality of the changing year that we experience. Bob Duggan argued that the summer goes through two distinct phases; by late summer, although the leaves are still on the trees, they are clearly becoming tired and drier. Flowers are fading and birds are already leaving. Late summer was his fifth season. This has helped me observe the world more closely and increasingly I am aware of this fifth season too.

We can learn from his example and use our knowledge of global diversity, not as a framework to force the seasons into, but as an inspiration – permission to observe the world and to decide what patterns have most meaning to us today.

How many seasons make sense to you?

The extreme may be found in Japan, where traditionally the year has been divided into as many as 72 micro seasons, each given a name to reflect a natural phenomenon, such as 'first Peach blossom' or 'first Bamboo sprouts'. You can even get an app for your phone called '72 seasons' that takes you through the natural Japanese year.

How delightful it might be to have our year defined, not by convention, but by close observation, reminding us constantly to take time out of the day to observe what is happening in life's natural patterns.

Of course, such an approach stretches what we usually mean by 'season' almost beyond recognition, but as a way of marking the passing year it is valid. Rather than blunt, broad stretches like 'autumn' we would be inspired to notice the finer details of the yearly cycle, and perhaps better notice the changes that we have unleashed.

Times of change

In times of intensifying climate change we can anticipate that the seasons will undergo further shift. In his book *The Nature of Winter*, Jim Crumley makes a grim observation: In the face of continued warming, along with many creatures, he predicts that the experience of harsh and bleak midwinter – 'earth as iron, water as stone' – may also become rare. For many of us this may soon be a memory but no longer a lived reality. The sparkle and wonder of icy landscapes are, he suggests, to be replaced by a prolonged anti-cyclonic gloom.

He adds that 'the wild year will soon be experienced in three seasons – a spring that lasts from February to May, summer from June to September and a drawn-out muddle of chilly and stormy autumn from October to January. The idea of four seasons will be reduced to a piece of music by Vivaldi.' In this muddy blending, it is not just our experience of winter that is threatened. Our autumns are already less like their old selves – Keats' season of 'mists and mellow fruitfulness' is too often now a tiresome progression of storms and drizzle.

It also seems we may be denied a specific storm season. Storms are not now contained within any one period but have become scattered through the year.

In his book *From What Is to What If*, Rob Hopkins, the initiator of Transition Towns, argues that addressing climate change is a 'project of the imagination'. By this he means that, if the rules of the planet have changed, and the systems and structures that got us here have been proven unfit for purpose, then our challenge is to take the opportunity to rebuild what we want to. Firstly though, we should let our ideas and spirits fly, if we have to re-imagine. . . everything. . . then let us be ambitious and imagine it all better than before. Let us take a lesson from the plants and become world weavers.

Begin today by imagining how good it could be.

The naming and rituals of the seasons may seem less of a serious issue compared to finding safe energy or curing pandemics, but it still remains a test of our ability to imagine anew, to think about the implications of a changed world. The seasons, as we recognise them today, reflect a dance between culture and recurrent weather patterns. As the nature around us adopts new patterns, so should our cultural response. On the list of things to re-imagine is how we mark and celebrate the turning of the year. In doing this we can be inspired by how different cultures have defined their seasons.

So, in the face of changing seasons, do we have sufficient imagination and daring to break with tradition and rethink how we describe our seasonal experiences?

Despite change, we can still hope

As worrying as it is to see the seasonal year unravel, we can take hope in one thing – life will find a way to adapt. Birds survived a burning planet to sing again, five times before life has been hit by catastrophes so extreme that they lead to mass extinctions, five times before life found a way, adapted and re-blossomed to continue world building. Nature has back-ups, deep underground and on the edges of space. Climate changes on our middle Earth, suspended between earth and sky, have very serious impacts and will demand radical change and adaptations but they will not finish things, really they won't.

Life will find a way, world weaving will continue.

This is not to underestimate the scale of our challenges, or the radical changes that are due, probably overdue. However, all is not lost. As Rebecca Solnit says 'there are usually cracks somewhere in the inevitable and the obvious. . .' we need hope because 'hope is an axe you break down doors with in an emergency.' To that I would add that we should treasure the cracks, because as we know life grows in cracks and finds a refuge there through the dark times.

She continues: 'I want to start over, with an imagination adequate to the possibilities and the strangeness and the dangers on this earth at the moment.' So here is another call to imagine everything better. Imagine, we should, because possibilities still surround us – a new world can bloom as it has before.

We need to ask ourselves if we have the resilience and ability shown by the rest of nature to flourish again. If we think maybe not, we need to learn from the resilience and creativity we can see around us in our gardens.

Chapter 8

What Comes Next. . ?
Gardening a Better Future

Biologists and ethicists are finding a common position. Humans have been the cause of much destruction, but to claim ownership of recovery is to fail to learn a lesson. The root meaning of the word 'apocalypse' is revelation. Our recent history has brought many upon us. In particular, we have had revealed our shortcomings. Wendell Berry wrote: 'We have proven we are not smart enough to take Eden by assault.' Surely we are not smart enough to recover a damaged world by ourselves?

Fortunately, alongside the revelation of our limits, has come the new insights into the resilience and creativity of nature. Other living creatures care little for our failings or pretensions and continue with world building as they always have done.

Sick with worry

Reflecting increasing stress about the future of life on earth, new terms are emerging for what Glenn Albrecht describes as 'psychoterratic' illnesses. These arise from the imbalance between our behaviour, how we see ourselves, and the collective well-being of our home. Solastalgia, climate grief and pre-traumatic stress disorder are all terms that have been coined to describe the damage done to our mental health by global destruction.

Despite our anxiety about the future, panic and sickness leave little room for imagining creative solutions. When we feel helpless in the face of threats, it is harder to see clearly what needs to be done, we often default to old habits and to blaming others. To address the complex problem of re-imagining and creating a better future, we first need to calm down our stress and the anxiety. Gardens and nature can help us to do this, firstly by the direct benefits they have on our mental health, and secondly by the lessons they give us of how to face upheaval, survive, and emerge again to build better than before.

Natural Resilience

We can be inspired by nature's resilience. We face the threat of climate chaos and mass extinctions, yet life has proved resilient to catastrophes before and regrowth has happened. Western science is only just beginning to glimpse the reality of a world that indigenous peoples have understood for millennia, learning from their close observations and respect for nature. No doubt this gave them resilience in the face of the destruction of their worlds and cultures. Resilience is defined as the ability to rebound after shocks and damage, and has superseded sustainability in the thinking of many experts. Resilience is an inherent quality of nature – life would never have got this far without it.

Ecological science reveals to us that life depends on webs and networks. Like the spider's webs, these can dissipate shocks and rebound because of the strength of the patterns and the connections. If we disconnect ourselves from the web of life, we have less ability to recover.

Let us not be complacent therefore. Humans and our artificial systems are not as resilient as the natural world. There is much we may lose, but still much to play for to save what we can.

Should we stay or should we go?

Together with other digital billionaires, Elon Musk has invested heavily in space exploration and is renowned for promoting the colonisation of Mars. Among the reasons he gives is that he believes that the risks to life on Earth mean that we should have a 'backup' for humans and life in general. In a posthumous message, Stephen Hawking also said he believed that humans should move beyond the Earth to survive.

With this kind of talk in the air, not surprisingly, there are increasing worries about the future – the word extinction is more commonly heard. At Eden Project I had many conversations with visitors, students and staff, who were worried about the extent to which life on Earth is vulnerable, and I heard people talk of their children's anxiety about the future. Not surprisingly, we see a rise in the stress related illnesses that Albrecht talks of.

Eco anxiety, solastalgia and related disorders may as yet lack widespread recognition, but I have no doubt that threats to mental health are on the rise. And I know that our gardens can help us.

Therefore, in this concluding chapter, I would like to tell two interwoven stories. Firstly, and hopefully not in too much detail, how life has faced huge challenges before and risen again, and therefore how we can hold some faith in the collective ability to survive coming storms. Secondly, I would like to explore the lessons that will help our own capacity to face upheavals and regrow afterwards.

So, for our collective reassurance I would like to take stock. How vulnerable is life really? To some degree extinctions are

j

certain but can we still influence how bad things may be? What hope remains?

Insights come from what has happened before.

Not the first and not the last, probably

A vital thing to remember is that if we do face a mass extinction event, this would be the sixth that we know of. At least five times before life has been devastated by catastrophic change. Five times before life got up again. How does that happen? How does life survive catastrophe? I believe that Musk is missing something. There are already backups in place.

The story of life's past helps us to understand how it has such resilience. One theory is that the origin of life occurred in deep sea volcanic vents. From the outset, therefore, life may have begun in conditions that we would believe impossible to survive. This was long before there were even protective cell walls, and shells and skins were unimaginably distant.

The separation into different kingdoms of life was an early step, the ancestors of modern plants, animals and fungi diverged approximately 1.5 billion years ago, probably when we were all still single celled creatures. Slowly, over billions of years, life gained complexity, evolving new capabilities and building the toolkit for future evolution. Crucial advances were not just evolving new bodies, but also creating those essential processes, such as photosynthesis, that enabled energy to be captured and allowed those bodies to be built from inanimate matter that was turned into living form.

The first evidence of photosynthesis, in cyanobacteria, dates from roughly 2 billion years ago. About 450 million years ago, the first land plants appeared. It is believed that some simple proto-plant cells engulfed cyanobacteria and these gradually evolved in partnership to become the chloroplasts that are the sites of

194

photosynthesis in all plants today. This demonstrates that cooperation and partnership began early and was a foundation for much of the evolution that followed.

Only about 900 million years ago did colonies of single celled creatures learn to co-exist so that the first multi-celled organisms could emerge. About 530 million years ago came the event called the Cambrian explosion – not a disaster but a flowering of life forms that produced the first true vertebrates, and it lead to the first animals colonising the land. Further leaps occurred in what is called The Great Ordovician Biodiversification Event.

About 460 million years ago the first land plants evolved, followed by the first insects. Only then could they begin to learn to work together to enable pollination. Slowly the pieces of a recognisable world were coming together. It wasn't all to be smooth sailing, though, there were setbacks to come

The setbacks and how we all survived them

Mass extinctions are defined as events that lead to the loss of at least half of the species in a relatively short timescale. Fortunately these have so far only occurred a handful of times. These events are often associated with the end of an era in the Earth's history.

Widely recognised as the first such event, the End Ordovician extinction occurred 440 million years ago. The cause is believed to have been climate shifts, rapid glaciation followed by a swing to rapid warming. Sea levels fluctuated and seas acidified, their oxygen levels falling too.

Later came the End Permian extinction – the greatest mass extinction in Earth history. This is sometimes called The Great Dying. Something like 97% of life died and this was the closest life has ever come to completely disappearing. Current theories are that the Great Dying was triggered by massive volcanic eruptions, probably in Siberia, that caused a greenhouse effect; Earth temperatures rose, seas acidified and lost oxygen again. Because of the risk of further climate linked extinction events it is vital to know what happened next.

The most important thing to understand is that although there was a Great Dying the lights did not go out completely, much was lost, yet enough survived to build again. The implications are crucial – life does not go back to square one after each extinction event. The most critical abilities for continued survival and continued world weaving still existed as a platform to rebuild on – photosynthesis, cells, the ability to transform the inorganic world into the living world, and the crucial partnerships that hold the web together. After each setback a new world was remade thanks to the survivors of an old world that had ended.

66 Million years ago, in the Cretaceous era, the Tertiary extinction affected three quarters of the life on Earth. This event spelled extinction for the dinosaurs, although before then they had already branched into smaller creatures that had much better chance of survival – including the songbirds that still grace our lives today.

It was not until a brief five million years ago that the first human ancestors appeared. We should not be too hard on ourselves, we are toddlers still – no wonder we are only just learning how to fit and cooperate.

So, to understand more of where our hopes can be grounded, let us talk a little more of survival – where and how does this happen?

Taking shelter

For life to survive great catastrophes like eruptions and asteroids, it helps to have refuges, places to shelter from the mayhem and to recolonise when it is safe. Where are these essential refuges?

Some life survives in the deepest ocean in volcanic clefts where it may all have started anyway. Deep sea caves beneath the Antarctic may also have sheltered life for thousands, or maybe millions, of years.

Life also takes refuge at great depths on land. A recent 'deep life' research project found that 70% of the Earth's micro-organisms; billions of living beings, maybe as much as 23 billion tonnes of 'dark life' survives at depths of up to 3 miles below the surface. Amazingly, it is not just the tiny bacteria that prove able to survive in these conditions, in deepest caves and mines, more complex life, worms and crustaceans may also be found.

Much nearer the surface, and yet much more important for our daily lives, is the seed bank – the buried store of plants yet to be, that shelter under our feet. Seeds are good at longevity, in dry cold conditions they can survive hundreds or thousands of years. In more normal soil conditions 50 years is more typically the limit of viability. The key point is that beneath our feet are entire ecosystems sheltering and waiting to grow again.

The most self-reliant form of refuge is extreme hibernation. Tardigrades and some nematodes have been shown capable of entering dormant states of such robustness, that they can survive freezing, boiling and even exposure to the cold and radiation of space. We know they can live in such hibernation, even frozen, for at least 30 years, possibly much more. Bacteria have recently been found that have been hibernating in deep sea trenches for an astonishing 100 million years. In their prolonged lockdown they can outwait a lot of human stupidity and a lot of 'cenes'.

Let's get out of here

Another important way that life survives threatening events, whether asteroids or just storms and winter, is by migration. Migration can seem worrying sometimes, unless we know what is happening, it looks like a vanishing. Lots of concern is rightly shown of the threat to corals by warming seas – it is tragic that we are losing the amazing underwater cities that have formed over thousands of years and these are irreplaceable, but the essential architects, the creatures who build them, have not all died, many of them are in their migratory forms and will build again when they find their new sweet spot.

Migration and refuge also happen in the skies. As we know, every square metre of air carries thousands of fungal spores, bacteria, pollen and tiny animals; each travelling long distances before they find new homes. Scientists have been looking up as well as down to determine the boundaries of life's adventure – spores of bacteria have been found at the edge of space – the stratosphere 1 kilometre up. Over time they will return to earth and return to life; no one knows how long this space refuge will continue to feed life back, but we do know life has another backup on the edge of the atmosphere.

A change is needed

Life also survives catastrophe by evolution and adaptation to new circumstances. This is happening constantly. For example, thirty years after the disaster at Chernobyl wildlife is thriving, trees are reclaiming the city, wolves, beavers and wild horses, some previously rare, are showing growing populations. We have already met the new variety of fungi that has evolved to harvest energy from radiation rather than from sunlight.

There are many other examples of continuing adaptation. In London, insects have evolved to survive in underground stations, never visiting the surface. Plants have adapted to live on toxic mine spoils, marine micro-organisms have learnt to digest plastics, creatures move to new locations, new climate zones, all are refugees taking future nature with them.

198

Give thanks to the backups and our future world makers and to the gardens where we can learn from them.

Lessons we can learn for an uncertain future

A test of our resilience and creativity came with the lockdown of the pandemic of 2020. During that extraordinary time, once favourite haunts were suddenly closed to us, even ones nearby that we had walked to daily. Travel to distant places, the chance to see the exotic wild spectacles and landscapes loved by magazines and TV documentaries, became distant memories. This underlined how fragile our connections to nature can become in times of upheaval. Yet there are positive shoots too – movements like School strikes and Extinction Rebellion reveal a growing frustration that the ongoing crisis is not addressed adequately by those with power, people are becoming tired of waiting and are taking action.

Meanwhile, in the USA, President Trump had appointed a coal industry lobbyist to head the Environmental Protection Agency. This followed decades of precedence, under every administration, of placing people with vested interests into positions of safeguarding. There is clearly something broken in political ethics. Amongst his opening remarks, the new EPA head said that whilst climate change is a 'huge issue' it should not be the top priority for the Agency as it is 'still 50 to 70 years out'. Clearly something is also broken in the agency's understanding or willingness to admit to climate science.

Not long before this, the renowned activist and writer Bill Mckibben published a book that gave a very different perspective. McKibben is often credited as being amongst the first to highlight the significance of climate change in his earlier book *The End of Nature*. Underlying this apocalyptic title was not a prophecy of a collapse of life but rather a recognition that if we define the natural world as one 'not excessively modified by humans' this state probably no longer exists. We have released a pervasive set of influences, including atmospheric change that can reach to the most remote corners of the vast Earth. Human footprints can now be found everywhere, even where we have never set foot, and it is time to let go of simplistic cultural myths of nature as an unspoilt Arcadia – distant and different from us.

John Muir wrote 'When we try to pick out anything by itself, we find it hitched to everything else in the Universe.' His perspective was based on observation of natural connections, yet there is a deeper reality revealed by the latest quantum physics too – everything connects to everything else.

We are linked by hidden webs just as every tree is linked. Nature is intimately interwoven into our lives and our bodies, and our fates are also woven together. Of course, in his writings, McKibben did not mean that nature as a resilient burgeoning force of creative evolution, had ended, but his argument is that an over-simplistic concept of how nature and humans relate, has changed forever. That need not be a bad thing, it may be a change that had to come.

McKibben has dedicated years to fighting climate change by forming the campaign 350.org to pressurise governments to limit the scale of pollution. Yet, despite these efforts, in his latest book he takes a startling new position – he argues that we should no longer see climate change as a 'threat' but rather as a present day reality to be adjusted to. Although there is much yet to play out, he argues that the switch has been thrown and we already live in a world that we have changed beyond recognition.

McKibben titles this new book *Making Life on a Tough New Planet*. As before. an old world has gone and there is a new one coming. He continues by emphasising that the rules are now different – the world no longer works like it used to, so everything we thought we knew about how to feed ourselves, run a stable and safe civilisation with adequate clean air, water and energy, are all things that we will have to relearn and approach differently.

Leaving the Anthropocene

I would like to finish on a note of hope. Most of the ethicists and scientists I refer to earlier have been informed by their understanding of ecology. They recognise that however much we could lose, however tragic the losses, life will find a way to flourish again. Things will be difficult, but thanks to the refuges and resilience that surrounds us, we will not be alone in world remaking.

As Anna Tsing says 'alone has no meaning in modern biological thinking'. If there is a world to be remade we will make it in partnership with many others.

Was naming the Anthropocene even a good idea?

Like the seasons, the naming of eras and epochs are not givens, they are choices that reflect our cultural beliefs. To reflect the world changing nature of our recent impact, scientists have chosen to name a geophysical epoch after humans the Anthropocene. However, not everyone agrees that this was the right thing to do. In a critique of anthropocentric perspectives, Natasha Myers writes:

'Precisely who is hailed by this Anthropos, that figure positioned at the helm of the Anthropocene? Anthropocenic rhetoric calls out "Man" as the agent of his own demise and simultaneously vaults him into position as the only viable saviour of the planet: "We got ourselves into this mess. We alone can get us out." '

She adds:

> 'Even as Anthropocentric analysis attempts to call our attention to — and finally hold us responsible for — the effects of our actions, it still figures humans as a singular agent, transcendent over and separate from some Edenic nature in peril. These narratives re-centre rather than de-centre Man as the agent with natural dominion over this planet's future.'

In a parallel vein, Glenn Albrecht, the Australian environmentalist and philosopher, feels that the importance and power of biological cooperation far outweighs the works of man, constructive or destructive. He argues, therefore, that the next era in earth history should be named the Symbiocene. He writes:

> 'The scientific meaning of the word "symbiosis" implies living together for mutual benefit, this is a core aspect of ecological thinking, symbiosis affirms the interconnectedness of life and all living things.'

He adds:

> "Nature viewed in all its aspects, cycles and interrelationships cancels out human pretensions to mastery over the planet."

Similarly, Donna Haraway emphasises that we will crawl from the self-inflicted damage of the Anthropocene as just one small part of the community of life that will start the rebuilding process. We will need a new way to relate with many other beings in grief and new world making, hopefully by then understanding more about our networks, allies and dependencies. She declares an ambition to move beyond the Anthropocene as quickly as possible.

Bringing it back to the garden

Returning now to our gardens, the small parts of this earth in our care. In the spirit of leaving the Anthropocene behind us as fast as we can, maybe it is time to recognise that these can be so much more than 'outdoor rooms' or 'places of display'.

Rather than saying "this country belongs to us", indigenous Australian elders say "we belong to this country". In response I suggest that our gardens are 'our country', the places we belong to, our observatories and our places to heal so that we can imagine better solutions. Gardens are where we can heal ourselves and, maybe, heal our personal relationship with the vast diversity that continues to sustain us.

Eden Phillpotts is credited with the saying: 'The universe is full of magical things patiently waiting for our wits to grow sharper.'

Just outside our windows, these magical things are waiting for us to step outside.

I would like to return to my starting question – what are gardens for? I believe that given the rich mutually-supporting community of life that lives alongside us, the answer cannot be determined by us alone. Just like the Earth itself, our gardens are their homes too. They will have a say in what happens, with or without us.

'Alone' has no meaning in modern biological understanding. Every member of our garden community is self-aware and self-determining, even the plants, contributing to the health of the whole and in constant communication with others. We should leave them enough space to live their own destinies; we do not have the right to do otherwise. As the scientists and ethicists have concluded, the interconnections and interactions revealed by ecology require us to change our world view. Nature, with all its wonders, cycles and creative transformations is more powerful and more important than us.

Deborah Bird Rose writes that indigenous Australian elders taught her:

'The living world is more complicated, less predictable, more filled with transformations, uncertainty, and fantastic eruptions of life's mysteries than is allowed of in ordinary thought.'

203

There are no grand solutions or strategies that will ride in to save us. We need to identify the best things we can do without relying on government. As Joanna Macy frames it, we need to change the 'Great Unravelling' to the 'Great Turning'. I have already referred to the Ark movement inspired by Mary Reynolds. Its aim is not to 'save the planet' by goals or grand strategies, sustainability policies, austerities, or codes of conduct, but to do what we can at the most local level, our homes. Most important of all, to stop killing and get out of the way.

Paul Kingsnorth agrees. He writes:

> 'Whether you have a field or a window box, this is not too hard. It is real action, and it has real, deeply valuable results. Best of all, it mostly involves doing nothing: just leaving things alone. Which in my opinion, is probably the best way to 'save the planet' in the end.'

Widely promoted 'green' actions like recycling or cycling are important, of course, but may not be adequate as personal responses to what we face, partly because so few are biodiversity oriented and because they rarely ask us to change our relationship with the living world.

Simple ways of connecting with nature

I believe that changing our perspectives and our relationship with nature are the essential first steps to recovery.

Fortunately, again, we do not have to travel to distant temples to begin this work, we can start by simply stepping outside, opening our senses and learning how to engage. There is no point trying to control the uncontrollable millions of our natural neighbours, let us find gentler ways of relating. Our times demand nothing less of us.

Earth's history teaches us that life must have two things – it must have safe refuge and also somewhere to return to after

204

migrations, somewhere to recover and to start again. Both of these are things we can provide in our gardens or nearby spaces .

We can follow Mary Reynolds' lead to create a safe haven for biodiversity. All it requires is to leave a patch to go wild, however much you can spare. Let the grass grow as overwinter shelter and lock the poisons away. If you don't have your own land engage with neighbours or nearby landowners, maybe a community Ark is possible?

Follow the model of forest bathing

Beginning in Japan, a practice called Forest Bathing has become popular across the world. Forest Bathing is in essence mindful exposure to nature for healing. It consists of focused walks in forests with all senses open – a chance to exercise, breathe in beneficial chemicals, observe, gather experiences and connect, if just for a while, to the web of nature.

Having lived through a year of restrictions on travel it suggests to me that we could also develop garden bathing, or perhaps just green space bathing. Wherever we can we should spend mindful time outdoors; to re-energise and boost our well-being to observe and to connect more closely with our natural community, for their benefit and ours. Learn what is living nearby and check it is in good health.

Foraging

Foraging for wild foods to add to our diet can inspire more adventurous meals, while nurturing a deeper connection with and respect for the land and its inhabitants. It also gives us a much more direct understanding of the food chain and the plants that wildlife depends on.

Foraging demands that we observe and learn. We must notice what is growing nearby, learn what it is and how and when to use it. For example the young tips of Nettles are tender and a prized ingredient in a forager's cooking, but left too long they become too fibrous to digest easily. So success relies on staying alert to seasonal change.

With a bit of creative thought, we can ensure that a good selection of edible plants are given room in our gardens. For example, choosing fruit bushes and trees instead of ornamentals, adding perennial herbs like Fennel and Sage to flower beds, and leaving some patches of plants like Nettles and Dandelions, which will also help the wild foragers too.

Foraging also demands respect. No successful forager completely strips the resource, we must learn the art of 'enough', leaving more to return to as we need it. The art of 'enough' has been lacking in our society. Fortunately there are many excellent guides to foraging, testament to the increasing awareness of its rewards. If it feels daunting, you can begin with small steps – just a few Dandelion leaves in your salad.

Make art together with nature

Another important approach to engaging with nature is through making and creative crafts. Making has also been shown to provide a boost to well-being and health. Many art and making projects can use natural materials that can be gathered from the garden, which again requires close observation of what is nearby and its seasonal patterns.

One important and inspiring approach to natural art is creating mandalas from natural materials. Mandalas are intricate geometric compositions based on circles. They have a spiritual meaning in Hinduism and Buddhism, where they are seen as representing the universe and are used as focus for meditation. Recently, this idea of crafting a radial pattern has been adopted by the Western world as a tool for therapy or relaxation.

Carl Jung, the Swiss psychiatrist, explored the psychological effects of mandalas while studying Eastern religion. Jung is credited with introducing the Eastern concept of the mandala to the West and believed them to be symbolic of the inner process by which individuals grow towards wholeness. Mandalas are sometimes referred to as 'sacred geometry'. Today we also recognise that mandalas follow the principles of fractal geometry, related to the patterns of natural forms like clouds and mosses. We know that contemplating these patterns is beneficial to our mental health – discoveries made long after Jung was writing.

In the pictures you will find examples from the work of two mandala artists, Diana Heyne and Susan Cook, who both work with gathered natural materials.

Of course, there are many other natural crafts to enjoy, such as making paper and inks, dyes, scents, sculptures and collages. All require us to get outside, observe and learn.

The next and better world – from engagement to action

Whether first wave, second wave or ongoing, pandemics are not the only upheaval on our horizon that threatens our connections to the natural world or our freedom to enjoy them. Recessions and political uncertainty are all promised for the coming century.

Thankfully, our nearby nature and our gardens will remain our refuge and sanctuary and an evermore crucial health-giver in future hard times, just as they have before. To paraphrase Deborah Bird Rose:

'Our Gardens are less predictable, more filled with transformations, uncertainty, and fantastic eruptions of life's mysteries than is allowed of in ordinary thought.'

Even if governments are slow, some innovators and creative

thinkers are on it already. First steps are being taken on the path to leaving the Anthropocene. First steps to the great re-imagining that Rob Hopkins called for. Unfortunately, solutions to difficult problems are not always easy. That's okay, we don't need easy we just need options, hope and determination.

In Project Drawdown, Paul Hawken has researched the 100 most effective responses to climate change, responses that work and can be applied from government to personal level to bring atmospheric carbon down again. Together, he finds, they add up to enough to make a real difference. We are beginning to build a roadmap for a safer future.

In an earlier project called Blessed Unrest, Hawken also describes the innovative and creative environmental and social movements by which people are improving the world and have been striving to do so for decades. If you are feeling disillusioned, I urge you to read it – it reaffirms that good people are there and are already doing their best for all of us.

There is lots still to do, yet we have models and maps emerging; here is a world to rebuild, let's start today. Not every setback is a mass extinction. Pandemics and other crises are also opportunities to learn from our gardens and nature's resilience, During our enforced hibernation we have had a chance to cocoon, to continue our imagining of what comes next and our transformation ready to fly again.

If there must be another extinction event let it be the End Anthropocene, clearing the way for the world that comes next. Let the Symbiocene begin.

Even in the darkness it is light somewhere. At every moment, somewhere on the Earth the sun is rising over somebody's garden and plants are waking to begin their day's work. Let's give thanks to the plants, the scum and all the diversity of life that is the foundation for resilience and will continue world weaving.

208

End-piece and Acknowledgements

There are many people to thank for this work. Some, and I never believed I would write these words, were my schoolteachers. My school was a violent place – the teachers more than the pupils. The greatest gift they gave me was an independence of thought and clarity of what I would not do. I came to realise that whatever they recommended would not be right for me. Essentially the teachers had only two ideas of suitable post-school life. You either went to Oxford or Cambridge, or worked in trading in the city of London. I did, in fact, go there for an interview but thankfully they spotted it was not a fit that would work for any of us, so I was a saved a life in suits that was not suited to me.

My family were not gardeners, we only had a small unkempt plot, but at the end of every violent day I would retreat there to unwind with the birds and the spiders for company, I must thank my sister Janet for my first interest in biology.

Eventually, against school advice, I took a job gardening with the local council. A year spent outside in every weather was a revelation; for the first time I really saw the seasons and learnt the names of trees. Amazingly, despite frost and drenching rain,

k

I felt healthier than ever and constantly fascinated. I knew that there was no way back, growing and the outdoors were then my life.

That experience took me to study horticulture at the University of Bath, something my school did not believe could be a viable choice, or even a real subject. I arranged it through the council's careers and education service. This was a narrative shared by many other students.

At Bath I was lucky enough to meet a mentor and great friend Peter Thoday, who was then presenting 'The Victorian Kitchen Garden' on TV. Peter was one of those rare teachers who could inspire, be an endless source of knowledge, and also fostered both critical thinking and practical application. Someone asked me once to name a book that made me cry, I had no hesitation – *Lehninger's Principles of Biochemistry* reduced many of us to tears. I learnt then that we can see the living world either as wonders, wholeness, colours and vibrancy, or as abstract chemical symbols and numbers.

From Bath I moved to Liverpool to do research under another great mentor, Professor Tony Bradshaw, who was a world expert on restoring industrial dereliction and who had discovered pollution resistant grasses evolving on the toxic heaps of Parys Mountain. Both Peter and Tony helped to shape the ideas in this book.

Both also lead me to Cornwall. Tony had worked for years on revegetating the spoil heaps of the china clay wastes around St Austell, Peter had joined Tim Smit and another great horticulturalist Philip McMillan-Browse in the restoration of the great walled gardens of the Heligan estate.

Around the kitchen table, Peter, Philip and Tim talked of the great garden Heligan could be once again, and slowly the seed that grew into Eden Project was being sown. When Tim eventually decided that a bigger garden was needed and a derelict china clay pit was where this should be, they needed someone who had experience of growing on spoil heaps. I had my shoulder tapped and then began the white knuckle ride that was building Eden, for which I thank Tim.

Between Liverpool and Eden I taught at the University of Reading; I thank the students and colleagues I met there, every one of whom taught me in return. And to the many colleagues at Eden and beyond who inspired conversations – Sharon, Kate, Sue, Gus, Ben, Dan, Andrew, Ian, Richard, Amelie and Juliet, I thank you all.

My greatest thanks to my partner Jane, who is my constant joy and inspiration, and who first had the idea of writing this during lockdown and indulged my endless buying of references.

Heartfelt thanks to my supportive and creative family and friends who have encouraged me for years, and special thanks to Rebecca Stoneham for the beautiful cover illustration. It all started as a blog I called 'A Wonder Through the Garden'. I want to also thank the readers who, through their appreciation and feedback, convinced me that the stories here were worth telling.

Another special mention goes to Susan Humphries of Arborfield school, who showed me what education could have been and should be. We visited every year from Reading with our own students and all returned enchanted after our visit to a school in a wood, a wood full of magical things.

Tony Kendle

Further Reading

If you are like me, the more you learn the more you want to know.

So below I have gathered some of my favourite references, many of which have informed my writing, and some that are not included within the book but also give more insights into the astonishing world that is our home.

More to read on garden wildlife

The pioneering study of the wildlife of a garden was conducted by a keen entomologist, Jennifer Owen. Over thirty years she caught and studied all she could find in her small Leicester suburban garden. The results were published in 2010, in her book *Wildlife of a Garden: A Thirty-year Study*, RHS press. This book is hard to find now, and at £200 a copy it is for real enthusiasts and specialists. It was not intended to be a popular 'how to' guide.

The breakthrough book inspiring the gardening public to deliberately foster more home biodiversity came in 2000 with *How to Make a Wildlife Garden* by Chris Baines, published by Frances Lincoln. Many have followed – Kate Bradbury, the RHS and Jim and Joel Ashton, and Chris Packham amongst them.

The Garden Awakening by Mary Reynolds had a different flavour. This bridged garden design and, I suppose, eco-spirituality; it is a very personal take by a 'recovering landscape architect' who made an impassioned argument for aligning our gardens with the ecosystem's natural tendencies rather than to impose a 'design'. Reynolds inspired a movement – We Are the Ark, that encourages people to leave wild spaces for nature. Through this network people share advice and mutual encouragement, but, aside from that, Reynolds shies away from giving direction.

More recently, in 2020, came *The Garden Jungle: or Gardening to Save the Planet* by Dave Goulson.

More to read on non-intervention

At a wider scale, the revolutionary approach of letting nature determine its own progression with minimal intervention has hit the wildlife conservation world as the concept of 'rewilding'. First trialled on Dutch polders there are now outstanding successes here in the UK. Most renowned is the transformation of Knepp Estate in Sussex, the story is told in: *Wilding: The Return of Nature to a British Farm* (2019) by Isabella Tree, published by Picador.

The approach is endorsed by George Monbiot in *Feral: Rewilding the Land, Sea and Human Life* (2014), Penguin.

Benedict Macdonald's (2020) *Rebirding: Restoring Britain's Wildlife*, Pelagic press, paints a compelling vision of a new national nature conservation strategy based on rewilding successes.

More on urban ecology and wildlife

A rich textbook written by one of the pioneers of urban ecology and an expert on lichens is: Oliver Gilbert, (1991), *The Ecology of Urban Habitats*, Chapman and Hall.

There is also Stephen Forbes & Tony Kendle (2013) *Urban Nature Conservation: Landscape Management in the Urban Countryside*, Taylor & Francis.

And, of course, much useful reading is available through the internet, such as important advice on why leaf litter is beneficial:
www.techtimes.com/articles/20789/20141122/leave-the-fallen-leaves-alone-heres-why.htm?fbclid=IwAR2UXd5y
LPkQtBexjFIhLAQhE3tKPc8FmsGHe-O3KS0Qeviep591x
Qo0CY0

An overview from the research team of Sheffield University, of why gardens are important for biodiversity:
www.wlgf.org/The%20garden%20Resource.pdf

Also you can learn more of the amazing recovery of nature in Chernobyl:
www.mymodernmet.com/chernobyl-wildlife-tours/

And of the plants surviving toxic spoils at Parys mountain in Anglesey:
www.visitanglesey.co.uk/en/things-to-do/activities/
landscape-parys-mountain/#.X5BoYEJKg1I

More to read on plant growth, senses and awareness

Daniel Chamowitz (2017) *What a Plant Knows: A Field Guide to the Senses*: Updated and Expanded Edition, Oneworld publications.

Peter Wohlleben (2017) *The Hidden Life of Trees: What They Feel, How They Communicate*, William Collins.

David Beerling (2017) *The Emerald Planet: How plants changed Earth's history,* Oxford Landmark Science, Oxford University Press.

George David Haskell (2018) *Songs of Trees, The Stories from Nature's Great Connectors*, Penguin.

And we have not finished discovering things – this journal article explains more of recent research into how flowers can sense and recover their shapes after damage:

Armbruster W.S & Muchhala N. (2020) Floral reorientation: the restoration of pollination accuracy after accidents, *New Phytologist*.

Whilst this tells of recent research into the sleeping patterns of trees:

www.vox.com/2016/5/19/11700690/do-trees-sleep-arbor-day

And also here are more findings on what roots can sense:

https://qz.com/959888/a-new-scientific-study-find-that-plant-roots-follow-acoustic-vibes-to-find-a-drink/

https://www.livescience.com/2331-roots-grow.html

These links reveal more of plants response to gravity:

https://blogs.scientificamerican.com/artful-amoeba/roots-down-shoots-up-but-how-does-a-plant-know-which-is-which/

http://theconversation.com/taking-plants-off-planet-how-do-they-grow-in-zero-gravity-45032

A more recent text moves beyond what we know of plant senses and begins to explore how we can understand their intelligence:

Stefano Mancuso and Alessandra Viola (2019) *Brilliant Green: The Surprising History and Science of Plant Intelligence*, Island Press

The breaking understanding that plants too sense and have problem solving capabilities, not surprisingly challenges our world view and people are starting to reflect on the implications, for example:

Stephen Harrod Buhner (2014) *Plant Intelligence And The Imaginal Realm: Beyond the Doors of Perception into the Dreaming of the Earth*, Bear & company.

Monica Gagliano (2018) *Thus Spoke the Plant: A Remarkable Journey of Groundbreaking Scientific Discoveries and Personal Encounters with Plants*, North Atlantic Press.

How too should we relate to maybe the oldest and largest living being on our planet?:
https://www.earthdate.org/pando-a-forest-of-one

More to read on human senses for comparison
Diane Ackerman (1991) *A Natural History of the Senses*, Vintage Press.

Guidance and activities created by the Sensory Trust: www.sensorytrust.org.uk

More to read on plant partnerships:
Ardetti, J., Elliott, J., Kitching, I.J. & Wasserthal, L.T. 2012, 'Good Heavens what insect can suck it' – Charles Darwin, Angraecum sesquipedale and Xanthopan morganii praedicta. Botanical Journal of the Linnean Society. 169 403-432.

Jeff Lowenfels (2017) *Teaming with Fungi: The Organic Grower's Guide to Mycorrhizae* (Science for Gardeners), Timber Press.
https://www.britannica.com/science/seed-plant-reproductive-part/Dispersal-by-water
https://www.nativeseeds.org/blogs/blog-news/how-to-grow-a-three-sisters-garden
https://www.gardeningknowhow.com/garden-how-to/beneficial/hover-flies-in-gardens.htm?fbclid=IwAR3dSmGgQMX1PFhc5X5S0TZMB5LlqyoCuQ_1Fy_W1kZ6zGQlfcRakUWcPJ4

More on microbes and tiny things
https://www.livescience.com/paris-zoo-blob-slime-mold.html
Gerald N. Callahan (2003) *Faith Madness and Spontaneous Human*

combustion, what immunology can teach us about self perception, Berkley Trade.

Ed Yong (2017) *I Contain Multitudes: The Microbes Within Us and a Grander View of Life*, Vintage.

Merlin Sheldrake (2020) *Entangled Life: How Fungi Make Our Worlds, Change Our Minds and Shape Our Futures*, Bodley Head.

Paul Stamets (2010) *Mycelium Running: How Mushrooms Can Help Save the world*, Ten Speed Press

Jeff Lowenfels and Wayne Lewis (2010) *Teaming with Microbes: The Organic Gardener's Guide to the Soil Food Web*, Timber Press.

Robin Wall Kimmerer (2003) *Gathering Moss: The Natural and Cultural History of Mosses*, Oregon State University Press.

More on soil, air and weather

William Bryant Logan(2013) *Air: The Restless Shaper of the World*, WW Norton

William Bryant Logan (2007) *Dirt: The Ecstatic Skin of the Earth*, WW Norton.

Robert Macfarlane (2020) *Underland: A Deep Time Journey*, Penguin.

Alan Watts (2014) *The Weather Handbook: An Essential Guide to How Weather is Formed and Develops*, Adlard Coles

Peter Wohlleben and Ruth Ahmedzai Kemp (2018). *The Weather Detective: Rediscovering Nature's Secret Signs*, Rider Press.

Gabe Brown (2018) *Dirt to Soil: One Family's Journey into Regenerative Agriculture*, Chelsea Green Publishing.

Jon Stika and Eve Stika (2016) *A Soil Owner's Manual: How to Restore and Maintain Soil Health*, CreateSpace Independent Publishing Platform.

More to read on foraging

Christine Iverson (2019) *The Hedgerow Apothecary: Recipes, Remedies and Rituals*, Summersdale.

Emma Gunn (2018) *Never Mind the Burdocks, 365 Days of Foraging in the British Isles*, Bramble and Bean Publishing.

Adele Nozedar (2015) *The Garden Forager: Edible Delights in your Own Backyard*, Square Peg

More on birds, their intelligence and their behaviour:

Michael Macarthy (2010) *Say Goodbye to the Cuckoo*, John Murray.

Jennifer Ackerman (2017) *The Genius of Birds: The Intelligent Life of Birds*, Little, Brown Book Group.

Jon Young (2013) *What the Robin Knows: How Birds Reveal the Secrets of the Natural World*, Houghton Mifflin Harcourt.

Graham R. Martin (2020) *Bird Senses: How and What Birds See, Hear, Smell, Taste and Feel*, Pelagic Monographs

David Allen Sibley (2020) *What It's Like to be a Bird* (Sibley Guides): *From Flying to Nesting, Eating to Singing – What Birds Are Doing, and Why*, Alfred A Knopf Publishing.

More on transient beauty and ways to engage with nature:

https://www.diygenius.com/fractals-in-nature/#:~:text=A%20fractal%20is%20a%20pattern, the%20biodiversity%20of%20a%20forest.

Leonard Koren (2008) *Wabi-sabi: For Artists, Designers, Poets & Philosophers*, Imperfect Books

For examples of flower tourism:

https://xyuandbeyond.com/flower-tourism/

There are quite a few books now on forest bathing, but why not start with the pioneer researcher himself:

Dr Qing Li (2018) *Shinrin-Yoku: The Art and Science of Forest Bathing*, Penguin.

Sarah Devos Katriina Kilpi (2020) *Forest Bathing: All You Need to Know in One Concise Manual – An Introduction to the Japanese Art of Shinrin-Yoku – A Practical Guide to Connecting. . . The Perfect Antidote to a Hectic Lifestyle*, Haynes manuals.

https://www.forestryengland.uk/blog/forest-bathing

More to read on nature and human health

Theodore Roszak, Mary E. Gomes, Allen D. Kanner (1995) *Ecopsychology: Restoring the Earth/Healing the Mind*, Sierra Club Books

Mary Reynolds (2016) The Garden Awakening: Designs to nurture our land and ourselves, Green Books

Simon Barnes (2018) *Rewild Yourself: 23 Spellbinding Ways to Make Nature More Visible*, Simon and Schuster.

Sharon Blackie (2018) *The Enchanted Life: Unlocking the Magic of the Everyday*, September publishing.

Joe Harkness (2020) *Bird Therapy*, Unbound.

https://www.medicalnewstoday.com/articles/324478

Verla Fortier (2019) *Take Back Your Outside Mindset: Live Longer, Prevent Dementia, and Control Your Chronic Illness.*

Isabel Hardman (2020) *The Natural Health Service: How Nature Can Mend Your Mind*, Atlantic Books

Sue Stuart-Smith (2020) *The Well Gardened Mind*, William Collins.

Lucy Jones (2020) *Losing Eden: Why Our Minds Need the Wild*, Allen Lane.

Also:

https://natureconnectionguide.com/10-amazing-ways-nature-effects-us/

More to read on changes and seasons

Jim Crumley (2017) *The Nature of Winter (Seasons)*, Saraband.

Lia Leendertz (2020) *The Almanac: A Seasonal Guide to 2021*, Mitchell Beazley.

Nick Groom (2013) *The Seasons: A Celebration of the English Year*, Atlantic Press.

More to read on natural making and arts in nature:

Emma Mitchell (2017) *Making Winter: A Creative Guide for Surviving the Winter Months,* LomArt.

Nick Neddo (2015) *The Organic Artist: Make Your Own Paint, Paper, Pigments, Prints and More from Nature,* Quarry Books.

Guy Tal (2021) *More Than a Rock: Essays on Art, Creativity, Photography, Nature, and Life,* Rocky Nook.

Jane Bevan (2013) *Craft From Natural Materials,* Bloomsbury

More to read on evolution and natures power of adaptation:

Professor Menno Schilthuizen (2019) *Darwin Comes to Town,* Quercus.

Jan Zalasiewicz (2012) *The Planet in a Pebble: A journey into Earth's deep history,* (Oxford Landmark) Oxford University Press.

Fred Pearce (2016) *The New Wild: Why invasive species will be nature's salvation,* IconPress

https://www.nationalgeographic.com/news/2012/2/
120221-oldest-seeds-regenerated-plants-science/

More to read on ethics, new biology and new beginnings

Glenn A. Albrecht (2019) *Earth Emotions new words for a new world,* Cornell University Press.

Bill McKibben (2011) *Earth: Making a Life on a Tough New Planet.* McMillan.

Bill McKibben (2003) *The End of Nature.* Paperback, Bloomsbury Publishing.

Glenn Albrecht's writing on Exiting the Anthropecene and entering the Symbiocene are available here:

https://www.humansandnature.org/exiting-the-
anthropocene-and-entering-the-symbiocene

Other key texts on this theme are:

Donna J. Haraway (2016) *Staying with the Trouble (Experimental Futures): Making Kin in the Chthulucene,* Duke University Press.

Joanna Macy, Molly Young Brown (2014) *Coming Back to Life: The Updated Guide to the Work That Reconnects*, New Society Publishers.

Anna Lowenhaupt Tsing (2017) *The Mushroom at the End of the World: On the Possibility of Life in Capitalist Ruins*, Princeton University Press.

Rob Hopkins (2019) *From What Is to What If: Unleashing the Power of Imagination to Create the Future We Want*, Chelsea Green Publishing.

More on Eden Project and Heligan:

Tim Smit (2010) *The Lost Gardens of Heligan*, Orion

Tim Smit (2016) *Eden*, Eden Project Books.

Philip McMillan Browse (2005) *Heligan: Fruit, Flowers and Herbs*, Alison Hodge

More on a school in a wood:

Susan Humphries and Susan Rowe (2012) *The Coombes Approach: Learning Through an Experiential and Outdoor Curriculum*, Continuum.